THE
TRANSISTOR HANDBOOK

First Edition

Cletus J. Kaiser

Published
by

C J Publishing
398 Wintergrape Ln.
Rogersville, MO 65742

ISBN: 0-9628525-7-0
Library of Congress Catalog Card Number: 99-96122

Printed in the United States of America

Table of Contents

Acknowledgments

The author is thankful to The Lord.

The author is deeply indebted to his family and many friends for their continued support.

Preface

Since the completion of The Passive Trilogy, which consists of *The Capacitor Handbook, The Resistor Handbook,* and *The Inductor Handbook*
requests were made for information on the active components in the same
type of reference handbook. This book provides guidance in using transistors, JFETs, and MOSFETs in electronic and electrical circuits. A handbook
on diodes call *The Diode Handbook*, has also been written.

As with all of my books, the chapters are arranged with theory and
construction information followed by application information. With all
chapters arranged in this manner, reading and using this books for reference
will be easier and faster.

Chapter 1

Transistor Fundamentals

Bell Telephone Laboratories announced in 1948 a three-section, solid-state crystal that would amplify called the *transistor*; a tiny, extremely light, highly reliable, and efficient device. The transistor could replace most low-power vacuum tubes applications. Transistors have many advantages over tubes due to their light weight, physical ruggedness, small size, low power drain, and not being a heat source. Although, when high-power, high-frequency energy is required, tubes may still be the better choice.

When a semiconductor PN junction is laboratory grown in series with another PN junction, a two-junction, three-section semiconductor device is produced. The device could either be a PNP or NPN type, depending on how the crystal was grown. This is the basis of a bipolar transistor. The center section is very thin and called the base. The base material of one polarity is sandwiched by the collector and the emitter material of the opposite polarity. The three terminals are called the collector, base, and emitter.

Figure 1.1 illustrates the circuit schematic symbols for the NPN and PNP transistors. An arrow is on the emitter lead of the device. The direction of the emitter arrow indicates forward-bias polarity. (Bias is discussed within the semiconductor theory section.) For the PNP transistor symbol, the arrow is pointing *in*. In the NPN transistor symbol, the arrow is pointing *out*.

Fig. 1.1 Transistor symbols.

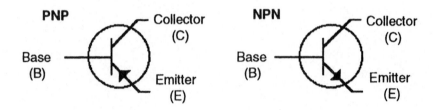

Semiconductor Theory

It is relevant at this point to give a basic description of semiconductors. Quantum mechanics shows that electrons in a solid can be represented as occupying discrete energy bands which are separated from each other by forbidden energy gaps.

Figure 1.2 represents the two outermost bands of any atom; the valence band and the conduction band, separated by a forbidden energy gap. It is the availability of electrons in the conduction band which determines the conductivity of a solid. Conduction can only occur if electrons arrive in the conduction band from the valence band. For this to happen, the electrons must receive sufficient energy to enable them to "jump" the forbidden energy gap between the two bands.

Fig. 1.2 Comparative energy levels.

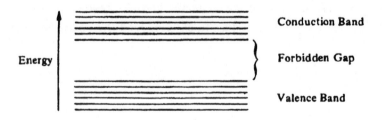

If the forbidden energy band is wide, which prevents electrons from appearing in the conduction band, the material is an insulator. Electrons will move from the valence to conduction band if sufficient energy is imparted to them. The application of a high electric field will do this. Thus, for all insulators, there is a specific voltage at which their insulating properties break down. In metals, the valence and conduction bands overlap with the result that electrons are freely available in the conduction band and can be persuaded to move between atoms when only a small voltage is applied. Thus, metals are good conductors of electricity.

In certain materials, the thermal energy imparted to some electrons at ambient temperatures is sufficient to enable them to cross the forbidden energy gap. For these materials there is a finite probability of electrons appearing in the conduction band. Therefore, these materials will exhibit slight electrical conductivity which increases with increasing temperature. Such materials are referred to as semiconductors. Although many semiconducting materials exist, the two most widely used are silicon and germanium, with silicon being the more common.

The width of the forbidden energy gap in pure silicon is on the order of 1.1 electron-volts at room temperature; the average thermal energy of the valence electrons is 0.025 electron-volts; thus, the probability of electrons appearing in the conduction band is small and the conductivity is very low. Conductivity can be increased if certain impurities are added to the semiconductor material.

Both silicon and germanium have a valency of 4. This means that a pure or intrinsic semiconductor will have a crystal structure as in Figure 1.3a shown on the next page. Each silicon atom binds with its neighboring atom to produce a stable configuration of eight valence electrons associated with each nucleus. If an impurity atom, such as arsenic, with a valency of 5, is introduced into the crystal structure (Fig 1.3b), then a free electron results from the binding of the valence electrons. This electron can be easily elevated to the conduction band and therefore contribute to electrical conduction. The arsenic atom can be said to have donated a free electron to the semiconductor and for this reason the impurity atom is known as a *donor* atom. The greater the concentration of donor atoms, the greater will be the number of free electrons and the greater the conductivity. Semiconductors treated with donor impurities are known as N-type. The existence of the free electrons does not constitute a net negative charge in the structure since associated with it is a localized positive charge on the arsenic atom. This positive charge also contributes to electric current but to a lesser extent. To distinguish between the two types of charge carriers in N-type semiconductors, the *free electrons* are known as majority carriers and the positive charges as minority carriers.

Fig. 1.3 Crystal structure of intrinsic and doped silicon schematic.

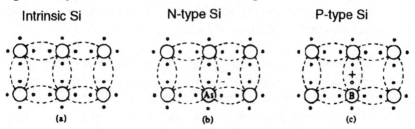

When a trivalent (valancy of 3) impurity, such as boron or indium, is introduced, the binding of the valence electrons results in a *space* or *hole* in the valence band (Fig. 1.3c). An electron from a neighboring atom will move to fill the hole, thereby causing a hole to appear in its place. The result is that a hole behaves similarly to a free electron but with a positive charge. It will contribute to electric current since a movement of holes in one direction is effectively the same as a movement of electrons in the opposite direction. Impurity atoms of this type are known as *acceptor* atoms and a semiconductor so treated is called P-type. In a P-type semiconductor, the *holes* are the majority carriers and the electrons are the minority carriers.

The process of adding impurities to semiconductors is known as *doping*. Impurity atoms may be either diffused into the pure semiconductor at high temperature or injected into the crystal structure using ion implantation techniques.

PN Junction
At the junction where N-type and P-type semiconductors are joined, the free electrons of the N-type and the holes of the P-type will diffuse towards each other. Diffused carriers leave behind fixed positive ions in the N-type region and fixed negative ions in the P-type region. These two regions with a fixed charge forms a built-in electric field which is in counter-direction to the flow of free carriers. The built-in electric field forms a potential barrier against free carriers (majority charge carriers). This potential barrier forms a depletion layer at the PN junction.

Both N-type and P-type regions of semiconductors are neutral by themselves at room temperature due to the constant generation and recombination of electrons and holes. Thus, there is no net positive or negative carrier in an unbiased (no voltage applied) semiconductor except at the PN junction regions.

When an external voltage supply is applied to the junction with the negative terminal to the N-type and the positive to the P-type, it will oppose the inherent potential barrier already existing at the junction. If the applied voltage is greater than the potential barrier voltage (0.7V for silicon, 0.3V for germanium), it will cause more carriers to cross the junction and an electric current results. In this arrangement, the junction is said to be forward-biased. If the voltage is applied with opposite polarity, then effectively the charge carriers in the N and P regions will be attracted away from the junction, resulting in an increase in the width of the depletion layer with an increase in potential drop across the junction which exactly opposes the applied voltage. Thus, very little current can flow and the junction is said to be reverse-biased.

For a junction that consists of N and P conducting regions separated by an insulating depletion layer, there is associated with it a particular value of capacitance. This capacitance normally degrades the performance of semiconductor devices and efforts are usually directed at keeping the capacitance to a minimum. As the reverse-bias voltage increases, the width of the depletion layer increases, thus, reducing the capacitance.

Three factors affecting the value of junction capacitance are:
- Junction area
- Applied voltage
- Impurity concentration.

A reduction in impurity concentration produces an increase in the depletion layer width for a given reversed-bias voltage, and consequently a reduction in capacitance. Minimum junction capacitance is aimed for in most products, but varactor diodes make use of this voltage dependent characteristic and are designed for specific capacitance/voltage sensitive applications. Values of junction capacitances can vary from less than 1 picoFarad to greater than 10 nanoFarads.

A junction of N-type and P-type semiconductors performs the function of a rectifying diode as shown by the voltage/current characteristic in Figure 1.4. This reversed bias current is temperature dependent; its value for silicon approximately doubles for every 10°C increase in temperature. Other factors affecting the reverse current are dopant concentrations and junction area. The value is typically of the order of 1 nanoamp at 10 volts, but can be less than 1 picoamp. The reverse current increases sharply when the reverse voltage becomes sufficiently high. This is due to avalanche breakdown across the junction and to a large extent is dependent upon dopant concentration. A decrease in dopant concentration will result in an increased breakdown voltage. Breakdown voltages can be in excess of 1000 volts.

Fig. 1.4 Voltage/Current (V/I) characteristic curve for a typical silicon PN junction.

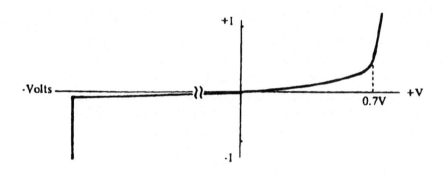

The Bipolar Transistor

When a second semiconductor PN junction is added in close proximity to the first, a three-section NPN or PNP device is produced. This device is a bipolar transistor.

When no external voltages are applied, the structure and potential distribution within the structure is in the unbiased state of condition. Under this condition the potential steps on each side of the center or base region are equal and there is no net charge transfer across the junctions.

When external voltages are applied to an NPN type bipolar structure, the base-emitter junction will be forward-biased (negative to emitter and positive to base) and the base-collector junction will be reverse-biased (negative to the base and positive to the collector). There will be a reduction in the base-emitter potential barrier and electrons will be injected into the base region from the emitter. These would normally recombine with holes in the base region, but if the width of the depletion layer of the reverse-biased collector-base junction extends sufficiently into the base region, most of the electrons will be swept across to the collector where they recombine with holes to form collector current.

For a basic understanding of how the device operates, consider positive or negative charges flowing from the emitter into the base region (positive for a P-type emitter or negative for an N-type emitter). A fraction x of these recombine with charges of opposite polarity in the base region and gives rise to base current. The remaining (1-x) fraction of charges reaches the collector-base depletion region across which they are accelerated into the collector. The algebraic sum of collector and base currents is equal to the emitter current. The ratio of collector to base currents is $(1-x)I_E = xI_E$; that is, $(1-x) = x$. For a given bipolar transistor, x is practically constant at constant temperature, and for normal bipolar action is $\ll 1$. Transistor current amplification can therefore be effected; a small increase in base current results in a much larger increase in collector current.

For high current gain performance, the number of electrons arriving at the collector from the emitter must be maximized. Therefore, the collector-base depletion layer must be made wider by lightly doping the base, and the base thickness made as small as possible. The number of electrons emitted is maximized by heavily doping the emitter with respect to the base, which inherently results in a low base-emitter breakdown voltage. The collector is lightly doped near the junction but heavily doped at the point where metal contact is made to it, and sometimes in the regions away from the junction, to reduce saturation resistance. This gives the desired low contact resistance. It is implicit in the foregoing discussion that a bipolar will function with the collector and emitter interchanged. This is so, but only with a low inverse current gain and lower operating voltages.

Basic Circuits

There are three basic transistor circuits. They are called according to that electrode or terminal (emitter, base, or collector) which is common to both input and output circuits (Fig. 1.5 - Fig. 1.7).

The three basic transistor circuits are:
- Common Emitter transistor circuit. (Fig. 1.5).
- Common Base transistor circuit. (Fig. 1.6).
- Common Collector transistor circuit. (Fig. 1.7).

Properties of the three basic circuits:*

	Common Emitter	Common Base	Common Collector
Input Impedance	Medium	Small	High
Output Impedance	Medium	High	Small
Current Gain	High	Less than 1	High
Upper Frequency Limit	Low	High	Low

*Depending on the base bias.

Fig. 1.5 Common Emitter transistor circuit.

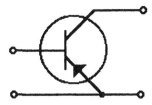

Fig. 1.6 Common Base transistor circuit.

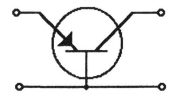

Fig. 1.7 Common Collector transistor circuit.

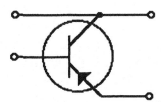

A simple transistor amplifier common emitter circuit is where a small base-current variation can produce a considerably greater collector-current variation. Since a small base-emitter signal current change produces a relatively large current change in the higher impedance collector-emitter circuit, considerably more power is developed in the output load. This amplification may have a gain of 20 to 30dB or 100 to 1,000 times the power.

Transistors with a slight forward-bias current operate as a class A amplifier. When operating without any bias, amplifiers are considered as either class B or class C. When operating with reverse bias, they are operating as class C. In both class B and class C, no collector current flows when there is no signal is applied to the input.

Operation Notes

Selecting semiconductor devices
The reliability of semiconductor devices is determined primarily by conditions of use. When using semiconductors, pay careful attention to any changes in conditions and be aware of the specifications of each device. Absolute maximum ratings and related precautions will be explained in the following pages. A good understanding of the absolute maximum ratings is necessary for selection of appropriate devices.

Maximum ratings
Absolute maximum ratings are used to specify the maximum temperature, voltage, and other limiting conditions under which a device can be used. The absolute maximum ratings are maximum values for operating and environmental conditions which apply to all products, and they must never be exceeded, regardless of the circumstance. The manufacturers have determined the absolute maximum ratings for their products, and as long as the semiconductor device is used within the ratings, the manufacturer should guarantee its performance and characteristics. When designing, it is necessary for the user of the semiconductor to take into consideration fluctuations in supply voltage, deviations in components, load fluctuations, and environmental changes. Also, design so that the absolute maximum ratings are not exceeded even under the worst conditions. If the absolute maximum ratings are exceeded, it is possible that immediate deterioration and/or damage to the semiconductor device may occur, and even if it still operates, a considerable shortening of its life is likely. Furthermore, semiconductor ratings are not independent entities. Temperature, voltage, current, and power all are closely interrelated and none may be exceeded.

Maximum allowed voltages
Maximum allowed voltages are the maximum voltages that can be applied between the emitter and base, collector and base, and collector and emitter

without damaging the transistor. If a maximum allowed voltage is exceeded, transistor damage may result. The manufacturer regards the breakdown voltage to be the maximum allowed voltage of a device, and guarantees that the breakdown voltage is higher than the rated voltage. For this reason, applying a voltage higher than the rated voltage may not cause transistor damage. However, taking into consideration device deviations, it is essential that the rated voltage not be exceeded. The emitter-base and collector-base junctions are both PN junctions. However, the collector-emitter junction interacts with both, and thus its maximum allowed voltage will differ depending on whether it is forward-biased or reverse-biased. The actual breakdown voltage is in a region in which the current increases very rapidly, and the voltage measured is that at which the current reaches a certain value. The absolute maximum rating has been fixed so that the entire transistor has margin with respect to the breakdown voltage. This margin varies by product such that the absolute maximum voltage falls within 50% to 80% of the breakdown voltage.

The absolute maximum voltage is rated at an ambient temperature of 25°C. Therefore, when the junction temperature approaches the absolute maximum temperature the absolute maximum voltage for 25°C cannot be applied. If it is, poor stability will result and there will be a danger of thermal runaway. Thermal runaway is a condition in which the current gain and cutoff current (I_{CBO}) rise together with the temperature and the base voltage (V_{BE}) decreases. If for any reason the temperature of the collector junction rises, the collector current increases, and this results in a further increase in the collector junction temperature. This cycle continues with the final result being damage to the transistor. In actual use, considerable margin must be established with respect to the rated values. A device should normally be used at a maximum of 80% of the rated values for 25°C.

Maximum allowed current
As a transistor is a three-terminal device, an absolute maximum current should be fixed for each of the terminals. However, normally only the emitter or collector current is rated. The maximum collector current is normally rated to be the current at which the DC current gain (h_{fe}) falls to 50% of its maximum value. The maximum peak current is rated at a value which ensures reliability within the maximum allowed junction temperature. In the case of a transistor by itself, the maximum base current is normally rated to be 1/3 the collector current.

Maximum allowed junction temperature

The junction temperature is limited by the relationship between temperature and life, and the characteristics of the materials composing the transistor. Furthermore, transistors use minority carriers and thus are easily affected by temperature. In particular, if the temperature rises in a reverse-biased collector-base junction, carriers are generated without relation to the signal, the operating point shifts, and in the worst case thermal runaway occurs and the transistor becomes damaged. For this reason, the circuit must be designed so as to prevent the junction temperature from rising. Transistor deterioration occurs quickly when the junction temperature rises.

To obtain high reliability, it is necessary to keep the junction temperature as low as possible. The maximum temperature of transistors is normally 150°C, however, recommend usage is at less than 100°C.

Maximum allowed power dissipation

The junction temperature rises due to consumption of electrical power within the transistor and increases in ambient temperature. The maximum allowed power dissipation is the amount of power consumption needed to raise the junction temperature to the maximum allowed rating.

Tj_{Max}. is the maximum allowed junction temperature. By using a heat sink for improved heat dissipation, the thermal resistance can be reduced and allowed power dissipation improved. Also, only DC allowed power dissipation is normally indicated. When a transistor is used for switching, the rating can sometimes be exceeded. In the case of saturated switching, the transistor moves between the saturated region and the cutoff region. In both regions power dissipation is low, and if the power dissipation of the transient state which moves along the load curve can be ignored, it can sometimes be acceptable for the operating point to move provided the voltage and current ratings are not exceeded. The maximum allowed power dissipation has been determined based on repeated reliability and damage tests, however, recommended use is at 75% of the rated value.

Maximum allowed storage temperature range

As an environmental condition for storage of a semiconductor product, temperature in particular is rated. The maximum temperature is determined by the maximum junction temperature and the package material. The minimum temperature is based on the package. Manufacturers normally rate the temperature range at -55°C to 150°C.

Secondary breakdown and Safe Operation Area (SOA)

The explanations to this point have been of ratings under normal conditions, however, if the operation involves inductive loads or sudden voltage and current increases, damage may occur which cannot be explained simply based on the average maximum allowed junction temperature. This is principally secondary breakdown and is caused by fly-back pulses, load shorts, or large load fluctuations. Secondary breakdown further increases the current after primary breakdown, and once a certain voltage or current level is reached, operation suddenly moves to a low impedance region, a high current flows, and transistor damage occurs. The area in which the transistor can be used without damage or deterioration and with high reliability is called the Safe Operation Area (SOA) and it is determined by the maximum voltage, the maximum current, the maximum collector power dissipation, and secondary breakdown.

Deviation of characteristics

Strict quality standards and control points are established for each stage of the transistor manufacturing process and transistors are produced in very large numbers. However, characteristics can change due to deviations in raw materials and slight changes in processing conditions. Deviations may appear not only among lots, but within one lot and even within the same wafer. It is not possible to correct these deviations by later adjustments. Principal factors affecting deviations include the thickness, diffusion density, depth, and resistivity of the wafer. Deviations appear in almost all of the characteristics. Deviations in the characteristics appearing in the data sheets are held within a certain range through lot inspections and 100% inspections.

Testing and inspection

Take special care with regard to noise produced by testing and inspection instruments. Voltage surges in commercial power supplies can cause deterioration or damage to semiconductor devices. Make sure that measuring instruments are sufficiently grounded. Breakdown voltages are frequently measured using a curve tracer or similar method. As the voltage is gradually applied make sure that the limit resistance setting is appropriate, and ensure that the rated voltage is not exceeded. Also, avoid bad contacts with measuring instrument terminals because a bad contact can cause surges.

Application Information

Bipolar Transistors

Small signal bipolar transistors have two prime circuit applications and are used in virtually all electronic products. They are:

- Switching - (Low-power output stages)
- Amplification - (Audio-frequency drivers and amplifiers).

Bipolar transistors are offered in both NPN and PNP polarities. Figure 1.8 illustrates both circuit symbols.

Fig. 1.8 Transistor schematic symbols.

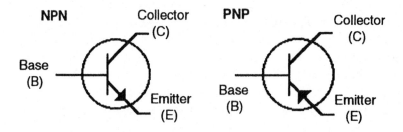

Dual transistors have two transistor chips in one package. Mounting cost and area can be cut in half. Configurations may be isolated, where two transistor elements are independent thus eliminating interference, common emitter, or some type of interconnect between the transistors.

Parameters when selecting a transistor:
- Transistor case size
- Saturation resistance
- Current gain (h_{FE} and h_{fe})
- Current handling capability
- Leakage currents I_{CBO} and I_{EBO}
- Temperature parameter variation
- h-parameters for linear applications
- Voltage ratings of all three junctions (V_{BE}, V_{CB}, and V_{CE}).
- Power ratings and thermal resistance
- Frequency response and/or switching times

Biasing and power supply polarity are positive for NPN and negative for PNP transistors. One junction will be forward-biased but the other junction will be reverse-biased. Since one of the two series junctions is reverse-biased, no current will flow until the barrier effect is lessened by a voltage. The more forward bias in the base-emitter circuit, the more the base-collector junction barrier is canceled and the greater the collector current, I_C. Saturation occurs in the constant current region of operation. The PNP transistor electron current operates in reverse to the NPN transistor. The voltage must be negative toward the collector. Forward bias for the PNP base will be negative in comparison with the emitter element.

The transistor is also used as an current amplifier. When a small current signal is applied to the base terminal (I_B), it is amplified in the collector circuit (I_C). This current amplification is referred to as "beta" or h_{fe}, and is equal to I_C/I_B.

Leakage currents such as collector junction leakage, (I_{CBO}), and emitter junction leakage, (I_{EBO}), are undesirable and should be as low as possible.

A conventional bipolar transistor is a current-driven device. Bipolar transistors are described as minority-carrier devices in which injected minority carriers recombine with majority carriers. A drawback of recombination is that it limits the device's operating speed. Because of its current-driven base-emitter input, a bipolar transistor presents a low-impedance load to its driving circuit. In most circuits, this low-impedance input requires somewhat complex drive circuitry.

Breakdown voltage is a design limitation for all semiconductors. The breakdown voltages must be taken into account for each combination of terminals. They are:
- V_{BE} (Base-Emitter Voltage)
- V_{CB} (Collector-Base Voltage)
- V_{CE} (Collector-Emitter Voltage).

V_{CE} with open base, (V_{CEO}), is of most concern because it usually defines the maximum circuit voltage.

Figure 1.9 illustrates a typical collector characteristic curve. Note that the negative collector-emitter voltage tells you that the transistor is a PNP type. Also that the output current increases with input or base current and varies very little with collector-emitter voltage.

Fig. 1.9 Typical collector characteristic curve for a PNP transistor.

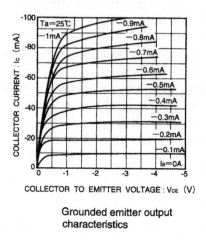

COLLECTOR TO EMITTER VOLTAGE : V_{CE} (V)

Grounded emitter output
characteristics

The operating temperatures of bipolar transistors are a frequent cause of failure. High temperatures are caused by hot-spotting, the tendency of current in a bipolar device to concentrate in areas around the emitter. Unchecked, this hot-spotting results in the mechanism of thermal runaway and eventual destruction of the device.

Layout of components
Heating of semiconductor devices must be avoided as much as possible, and they must be protected from surge damage. For this purpose:
1) Do not place a heat source near a device.
2) Dust collects on high-voltage circuits. Make sure dust does not collect on devices.
3) Exercise caution with high-voltage, high-frequency wiring and associated windings. These kinds of wiring can cause device damage through surges.

Land pattern
In particular, to allow sufficient heat dissipation from the collector fins of power type transistors, make the pad dimensions as large as possible.

Moving and storage
Observe the following precautions when moving or storing transistors:
1) Avoid high humidity and high temperature.
2) Avoid static electricity (do not store in Styrofoam boxes). Store
 in containers in which there is little generation of static electricity.
3) Do not store in a location where harmful gases are produced.
4) Store in a location where there is little dust.
5) Make sure that no heavy loads are placed on devices in storage.
6) Do not store for a prolonged time after forming leads since rust may
form due to slight damages caused by forming.
7) Avoid sudden temperature changes during storage and when
removing from storage.

Handling transistors during the manufacturing process
When handling transistors during manufacturing, take care not to subject
them to mechanical, thermal, electrical, or chemical stresses.

Forming leads
When forming leads, make sure that the force applied to the lead is not
transmitted to the package. Also, when applying force to the lead, make sure
the stress is released.
1) Do not hold the package when bending a lead.
2) Do not pull on a lead.
3) Do not bend the lead at the base. Bend the lead at a point at least 1.0mm
from its base.
4) Do not repeatedly bend a lead.
5) Do not damage a lead. The surface of the lead is solder, and if the metal
underneath becomes exposed it will oxidize and impair soldering.

Mounting on the board
Observe the same precautions as for forming leads. Also:
1) Make sure that the distance between the leads is the same as the distance
between the insertion holes in the board. If not, form the leads before
insertion.
2) Do not pull hard on the leads when inserting them in the board.

Soldering

1) Flux

Use a rosin based flux. Do not use a highly acidic or alkaline flux.

2) Soldering

Semiconductor devices do not tolerate heat well, thus soldering must be completed as quickly as possible. Ground the solder bath and iron.

3) Cleaning

Some detergents may dissolve the package, weaken the seal, or efface the inscription. If the transistors are cleaned by ultrasonic cleaning, make sure the output is at a level which will not subject the transistors to stress. Do not allow the board or device to come in contact with the vibration source.

Mounting transistors

Using a soldering iron

Soldering with a soldering iron can easily create thermal and mechanical stresses which will damage the package, and it can also cause misalignment. For these reasons, we recommend that you only use a soldering iron for testing and repair work.

Reflow soldering

This method involves applying soldering paste on the board by screen printing or other technique, mounting the product, and then conveying it into an oven where it is soldered by heating. Preheating to prevent package damage, board warping, deformation, and solder paste fly-off is recommend.

Power Transistors

Power transistors may use a Darlington connection for high DC current gain. This package has two transistors in one package.

Power transistors may also have built-in zener diodes, resistors, and damper diodes.

Temperature ratings
To ensure normal operation, allowed temperature for operation and storage have been established by the manufacturer.

Safe Operating Area (SOA)
In addition to allowed ranges for V_{CE}, I_C, and P_C, power transistors also have voltage, current, and pulse width restrictions. This is due to the fact that excessive voltage, current, and pulse width can cause secondary breakdown, leading to a weakening of the PN junctions and a damaged transistor.

Ranges 1 through 4 of the Safe Operating Area (SOA) shown in Figure 1.10 are determined based on the following factors:
- *Range 1* - This is limited by the maximum collector current. The maximum collector current is determined as an actual allowed range of use of h_{FE}.
- *Range 2* - This is limited by the thermal resistance, with the limit being the line = $P_{CMax.}$ = I_C x V_{CE}.
- *Range 3* - This is limited by secondary breakdown.
- *Range 4* - This is limited by the collector-emitter breakdown voltage.

Fig. 1.10 Safe Operating Area (SOA).

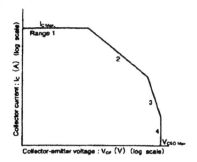

Power rating

Maximum collector power dissipation ratings (P$_C$) have been established both for a fixed ambient temperature (T$_A$) and a fixed case temperature (T$_C$), and for use with and without heat sinks.

Attachment to heat sink fins

The use of heat sink fins with power transistors will dissipate the heat generated by the transistor and lower the temperature of the junction. However, an inappropriate method of attachment will result not only in a failure to dissipate heat, but may damage the transistor as well.

Observe the following precautions when attaching transistors to heat sink fins:

A) If the fin is warped or there are burrs in the insertion holes, not only will insufficient heat dissipation result, but the transistor may be damaged as well. For this reason, observe the following:

1. The heat sink should not be more than 0.05mm out of true.
2. The insertion holes should be beveled.
3. The holes should be an appropriate size.
4. Ensure that no foreign matter is trapped between the transistor and the heat sink.

B) If the transistor is not attached with sufficient torque, full heat dissipation will not be obtained. At the same time, excessive torque may damage the transistor or break leads. Check manufacturer's data sheet for recommended torque.

C) Use self-tapping screws to attach the transistor to the heat sink. Do not use flat or round head screws as they may apply abnormal stress to the transistor.

D) Silicon grease applied between the transistor and the heat sink to reduce thermal resistance should be thin and even. Also, some types of silicon grease can damage the transistor or impair its performance, therefore, select the type of grease carefully.

E) Attach the transistor to the heat sink before soldering it. If the transistor is attached after being soldered, the leads and package may be damaged due to excessive stress.

RF Transistors

RF transistors must have very low path resistances and low lead inductances which require special leadframes. Due to the need for very low parasitic parameters, especially low transistor capacitances, it is necessary for RF transistors to be microstructures on a chip in order to keep the parasitic parameters as low as possible.

RF transistors have these features:
- High power gain
- Low noise figure
- Low cross modulation
- Small lead inductances
- High transition frequency
- Small feedback capacitance.

Circuit applications include:
- Oscillator applications
- High-speed logic applications
- Wide-band antenna amplifiers
- Self-oscillating RF mixer stages
- Controlled and uncontrolled prestages
- Low-noise and high-gain broadband amplifiers
- RF amplifiers and wireless communication RF amplifiers for cellular front ends or keyless entry circuits.

Types of high-frequency transistor applications:
- NPN Transistors with cut-off frequencies up to 20 GHz in order to obtain low noise figures at the operatings frequencies for cellular phone receiver front ends or other antenna booster circuits.
- Dual Gate MOSFETs are used in television tuner applications to obtain proper cross modulation performance in gain controlled prestages where the second gate is used for the control function.
- MOS Micro Integrated Circuits have an integrated biasing network in a 4-lead SMD package. Dual circuits in a single 6-lead SMD package save space in typical front ends for dual band television tuner applications.

Digital Transistors

Transistors with built-in resistors are sometimes called digital transistors. Digital transistors have built-in bias resistors that enable the configuration of an inverter circuit without connecting external input resistors (Fig. 1.11). Therefore, the three terminals are IN, OUT, and GND. The bias resistors consist of thin-film resistors with complete isolation to allow positive biasing of the input. They also have the advantage of almost completely eliminating parasitic effects. Only the on/off conditions need to be set for operation, making design easy. NPN and PNP polarities are available.

Fig. 1.11 Digital transistor equivalent circuit.

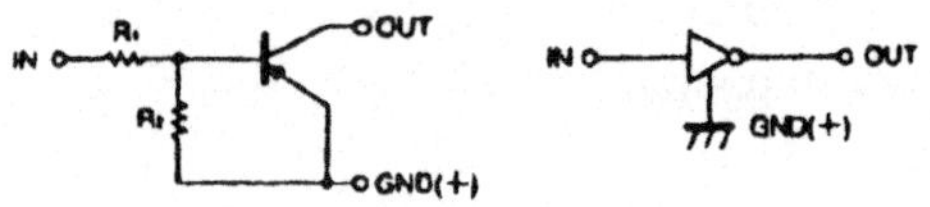

Digital transistor drivers have a built-in zener diode for strong protection against reverse surges due to low loads.

Dual digital transistors are ideal for power switching circuits in power management.

Precautions when measuring and handling digital transistors

When measuring and mounting digital transistors, the likelihood increases that open-circuited terminals will individually come in contact with the human body, measuring instruments, the work stand, soldering iron, or other equipment. In addition to electro-static discharge, leakage from electrical equipment will damage the transistors, therefore, care must be taken that no current leakage from an AC power source occurs through the terminals of the measuring instrument.

Insulated Gate Bipolar Transistors (IGBTs)

Introduction

Insulated Gate Bipolar Transistors (IGBTs) are MOS gated high voltage switching devices combining the best features of MOSFETs and bipolar transistors. These devices have the high input impedance of a MOSFET and the low on-state conduction loss of a bipolar transistor. The conductivity of the epitaxial drain region of a conventional MOSFET is dramatically increased (modulated) by injected carriers; this mechanism results in a significant reduction in the device on-resistance. Circuit symbols are shown in Figure 1.12.

The IGBT is ideal for many high-voltage switching applications operating at moderate frequencies where low conduction losses are essential. Such applications are:

- Power supplies
- AC and DC motor controls
- Drivers for solenoids, relays, and contactors.

IGBTs are useful at higher switching frequency than is generally practical with power Darlington transistors.

Fig. 1.12 IGBTs circuit symbols.

N-Channel Enhancement-mode   P-Channel Enhancement-mode

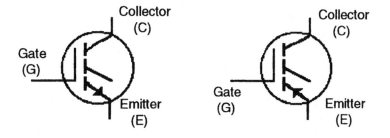

Circuit Design Precautions

- Gate Voltage Rating - Never exceed the gate-voltage rating of V_{GEMax}. Exceeding the rated V_{GE} can result in permanent damage to the oxide layer in the gate region.

- Gate Termination - The gates of these devices are essentially capacitors. Circuits that leave the gate open-circuited or floating should be avoided. These conditions can result in turn-on of the device due to voltage build-up on the input capacitor due to leakage currents or pickup.

- Gate Protection - These devices do not have an internal monolithic zener diode from gate to emitter. If gate protection is required, an external zener is recommended.

Turn-on in IGBTs is often intentionally slowed to control the reverse recovery of the free-wheeling diode common to inductive switching circuits. The IGBT can be used to limit high peak recovery current in the diode, but at a sacrifice in turn-on speed and loss. If reduction in rectifier peak recovery current is required, small saturating inductors may be used in the recovery circuit.

When turning off an inductive load, a switch circuit must sustain a voltage higher than the load driving voltage. Left to itself, the switch must sustain this voltage while conducting full current. The turn-off Safe Operating Area (SOA) describes a locus of maximum permissible combinations of voltages and current across the switch during turn-off which will not cause improper operation of the switch. IGBTs are generally rated for switching at 80% of the static blocking device rating.

Use the IGBT, with its low switching loss, in active inductive switching from full current, the so-called "hard switch" or Pulse Width Modulated (PWM) circuits, particularly at switching frequencies above 10KHz.

In PWM circuits, inductive switching usually involves clamping the inductive voltage rise to some sink, such as the DC buss. The higher turn-off SOA voltage of the IGBT, may make it the preferred solution for DC buss voltages above 300V to 400V. The IGBT can provide fault current limiting for a few microseconds in PWM circuits, allowing for the orderly shut down of the circuit form the gate drive.

Summary

A MOS-gate-controlled power device, the IGBT, has the desirable feature of a very low on-resistance similar to that of a bipolar transistor, but is capable of maintaining gate control of the anode current over a wide range of operating conditions. The low on-resistance is due to conductivity modulation of the N epitaxial layer equivalent to the extended drain in a power MOSFET; this carries with it the penalty of slow switching compared with that of a conventional power MOSFET

Handling IGBTs

Insulated gate bipolar transistors are susceptible to gate-insulation damage by the electro-static discharge of energy through the devices. When handling these devices, care should be exercised to assure that the static charge built in the handler's body capacitance is not discharged through the device. With proper handling and application procedures, however, IGBTs are currently being extensively used in production by numerous equipment manufacturers in military, industrial, and consumer applications, with virtually no damage problems due to electro-static discharge. IGBTs can be handled safely if the following basic precautions are taken:

1) Tips of soldering irons should be grounded.

2) Devices should never be inserted into or removed from circuits with power on.

3) Prior to assembly into a circuit, all leads should be kept shorted together either by the use of metal shorting springs or by the insertion into conductive material.

4) When devices are removed by hand from their carriers, the hand being used should be grounded by any suitable means; for example, with a metallic wristband.

Unijunction Transistor

A unijunction transistor (UJT) is a three terminal device with characteristics very different from the conventional two-junction, bipolar transistor. Figure 1.13 illustrates the circuit symbol.

Fig. 1.13 Unijunction circuit symbol.

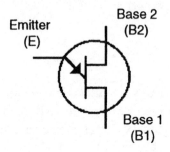

The UJT is a pulse generator with the trigger or control signal applied at the emitter. This trigger voltage is a fraction (η) of interbase voltage V_{bb}. The emitter terminal does not inject current into the base region until its voltage reaches peak voltage, V_p. Once V_p is reached, the base circuit conducts and a positive pulse appears at the B1 terminal and a negative pulse appears at the B2 terminal. The UJT incorporates a negative resistance region, a low emitter current, and a high output pulse current at both B1 and B2 terminals, making it an ideal pulse trigger.

Applications include:
- Timers
- Oscillators
- SCR triggers
- Frequency dividers
- Sawtooth generators
- Stable voltage sensing.

Figure 1.14 illustrates the characteristic curve of the unijunction transistor. The curve shows that the unijunction emitter blocks current flow until its voltage reaches Vp, then conducts.

Fig. 1.14 Unijunction transistor characteristic curve.

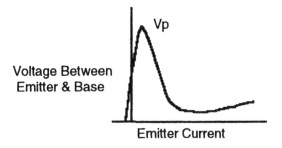

The basic specifications of a UJT are:
- Ip - The peakpoint emitter current
- R_{bb} - The interbase resistance of the UJT
- η - The intrinsic standoff ratio which defines Vp
- $V_{bb(max.)}$ - The maximum interbase voltage that can be applied to the UJT.

Basic Circuits

Fig. 1.15 PNP Common collector amplifier circuit.

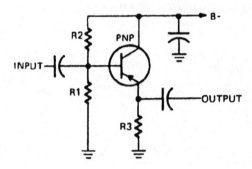

Fig. 1.16 NPN Common collector amplifier circuit.

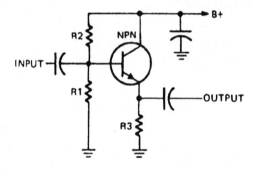

Fig. 1.17 PNP Common base amplifier circuit.

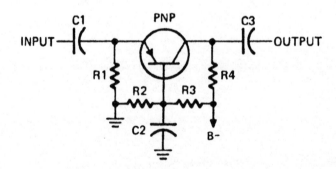

Fig. 1.18 NPN Common base amplifier circuit.

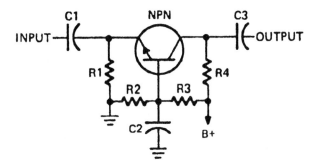

Fig. 1.19 PNP Common emitter amplifier circuit.

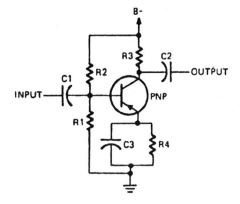

Fig. 1.20 NPN Common emitter amplifier circuit.

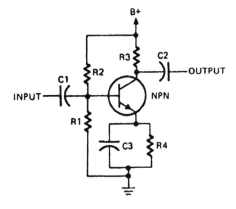

Fig. 1.21 Transistor OR Gate.

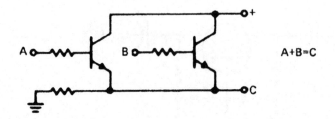

A+B=C

Fig. 1.22 Transistor AND Gate with the output isolated from the inputs..

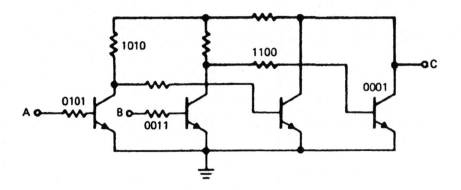

Chapter 2

JFETs

The theoretical description of a Field-Effect Transistor (FET) made by Shockley in 1952 paved the way for development of a classic electronic device which provides the designer the means to accomplish nearly every circuit function. At one time, the FET was known as a "unipolar" transistor. The term refers to the fact that current is transported by carriers of one polarity (majority), whereas in the conventional bipolar transistor carriers of both polarities (majority and minority) are involved.

Field-effect transistors consist essentially of an electrically conducting channel (either N-type or P-type) whose conductivity may be controlled by applying a voltage to a controlling gate terminal. The FET is a voltage controlled device; a small change in input voltage causes a large change in output current. Bipolar transistors are often termed minority carrier transistors by virtue of the minority carrier current through the base. However, the field-effect transistor relies on majority carrier current for its operation.

The family tree of FET devices may be divided into two main branches: Junction FETs (JFETs) and Insulated Gate FETs (or MOSFETs, Metal Oxide Semiconductor Field-Effect Transistors). JFETs are inherently depletion-mode devices only, and are available in both N-channel and

P-channel configurations. MOSFETs are available in both enhancement and depletion modes, and also exist as both N-channel and P-channel devices. The two main FET groups depend on different phenomena for their operation, and will be discussed in separate chapters.

This chapter provides an insight into the nature of the JFET, the basic characteristics, terminology, parameters, and typical applications.

Junction FETs (JFETs)

Introduction
JFET operation involves an electric field which controls the flow of a current through the device. In contrast, a bipolar transistor employs a small input current to control a large output current. The three JFET terminals are called the source, drain and gate are analogous to the emitter, collector, and base of a bipolar transistor. The terms N-channel and P-channel refer to the material to which the drain and source are connected.

The operation of a P-channel JFET is similar to the N-type except that voltage polarities and current directions are reversed. The circuit symbols for both N-channel and P-channel are shown in Figure 2.1. The arrows on the gate show the polarity of the gate-channel junction.

NOTE: The direction of the arrow at the gate gives the direction of current flow for the forward-bias condition of the junction. In practice, however, it is always reverse-biased.

Fig. 2.1 Circuit symbols for Junction FETs.

N-channel JFET   P-channel JFET

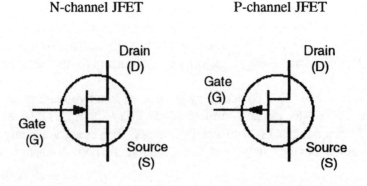

In an N-channel JFET, the drain and source connections are made to the N-channel and the gate is connected to the P material. The N material provides a current path from the drain. To the source to turn on the current, an N-channel JFET is biased so that the drain is positive in reference to the source. On the other hand, a P-channel JFET with a gate of N-type material would be biased in reverse.

As with any reverse-biased PN junction, a depletion region is formed which increases as the reverse gate voltage is increased. This depletion region, being devoid of majority carriers, reduces the channel drain-source current, (I_{DS}). As a result, the drain-source current is controlled by the gate voltage. As the gate voltage is increased, the drain-source current is increased. The figure of merit, g_{fs}, is the ratio of drain-source current to gate voltage. This ratio is the JFET transconductance.

This transistor consists of a piece of semiconductor material (usually silicon) which constitutes a channel for the majority carrier flow. The magnitude of this current is controlled by a voltage applied to a gate, which is a reverse-biased PN junction formed along the channel. Implicit in this description is the fundamental difference between the JFET and bipolar devices; when the JFET junction is reverse-biased, the gate current is practically zero, whereas the base current of the bipolar transistor is always some value greater than zero. The JFET is a high-input resistance device, while the input resistance of the bipolar transistor is comparatively low. If the channel is doped with a donor impurity, N-type material is formed and the channel current will consist of electrons. If the channel is doped with an acceptor impurity, P-type material will be formed and the channel current will consist of holes. N-channel devices have greater conductivity than P-channel types, since electrons have higher mobility than do holes; thus N-channel JFETs are approximately twice as efficient conductors compared to their P-channel counterparts.

In addition to the channel material, a JFET contains two ohmic (nonrectifying) contacts: the source and the drain. Since a symmetrical geometry is formed in the idealized JFET chip, it is immaterial which contact is called the source and which is called the drain; the JFET will conduct current equally well in either direction and the source and drain leads are usually interchangeable.

The JFET functions if the gate is connected to the source, then the applied voltage (V_{DS}) will appear between the gate and the drain. Since the PN junction is reverse-biased, little current will flow in the gate connection. The potential gradient established will form a depletion layer where almost all the electrons present in the N-type channel will be swept away. The most depleted portion is in the high field between the gate and the drain, and the least depleted area is between the gate and the source. Because the flow of current along the channel from the (positive) drain to the (negative) source is really a flow of free electrons from source to drain in the N-type silicon, the magnitude of this current will fall as more silicon becomes depleted of free electrons. There is a limit to the drain current (I_D) which increased V_{DS} can drive through the channel. This limiting current is known as I_{DSS} (Drain-to-source current with the gate shorted to the source).

The output characteristics of an N-channel JFET with the gate short-circuited to the source, is the initial rise in I_D is related to the build-up of the depletion layer as V_{DS} increases. As the curve approaches the level of the limiting current I_{DSS}, the I_D begins to be pinched off. The physical meaning of this term leads to one definition of pinch-off voltage, Vp, which is the value of V_{DS} at which the maximum I_{DSS} flows.

Consider the case where $V_{DS} = 0$, and where a negative voltage V_{GS} is applied to the gate. Again, a depletion layer has built up. If a small value of V_{DS} were now applied, this depletion layer would limit the resultant channel current to a value lower than would be the case for $V_{GS} = 0$. In fact, at a value of $V_{GS} > Vp$, the channel current would be almost entirely cut off. This cut-off voltage is referred to as the gate cut-off voltage, and may be expressed by the symbol Vp or by $V_{DS(off)}$. Vp has been widely used in the past, but $V_{DS(off)}$ is now more commonly accepted since it eliminates the ambiguity between gate cut-off and drain pinch-off.

The mechanisms of the above cases react together to provide a family of output characteristics. The area below the pinch-off voltage locus is known as the ohmic region; the area above pinch-off is the current saturation region. JFETs operating in the current saturation region make excellent amplifiers. Note that in the ohmic region both V_{GS} and V_{DS} control the channel current, while in the current saturation region V_{DS} has little effect and V_{GS} essentially controls the I_D.

The P-channel JFET works in precisely the same way as the N-channel JFET. In manufacture, the planar process is essentially reversed, with the acceptor impurity diffused first onto N-type silicon, and the donor impurity diffused later to form a second N-type region and leave a P-type channel. In the P-channel JFET, the channel current is due to hole movement, rather than to electron mobility. Consequently, all the applied polarities are reversed, along with their directions and the direction of current flow.

In summary, a junction field-effect transistor consists essentially of a channel of semiconductor material along which a current may flow whose magnitude is a function of two voltages, V_{DS} and V_{GS}. When V_{DS} is greater than V_P, the channel current is controlled largely by V_{GS} alone, because V_{GS} is applied to a reverse-biased junction. The resulting gate current is extremely small.

That was a brief overview of the how a junction field-effect transistor operates. Detailed junction field-effect transistor theory of operation and circuit operation characteristics begins on the next page.

JFET Semiconductor Theory

The JFET consists of a channel of N-type or P-type semiconductor material embedded in a semiconductor region of opposite polarity.

Figure 2.2 shows an idealized N-channel JFET where the P-type region is the controlling gate and the N-type channel has electrical connections made at both ends (source and drain). Electrical connection to the gate is made at either the substrate or top gate contact. The controlling gate is isolated from the conducting channel by virtue of the reverse-biased PN junction.

Fig. 2.2 Idealized representation of an N-channel JFET section.

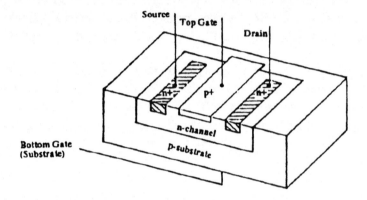

To understand how the JFET works, one must consider its operation under two distinct bias conditions:
- JFET working *below* saturation
- JFET working *in the* saturation region.

Figure 2.3 illustrates the idealized cross sectional diagram of an N-channel JFET with a positive voltage, V_{DS}, applied between drain and source, and with the gate shorted to the source. Since the drain is positive with respect to source and gate, the drain-gate junction will always be reverse-biased and practically no gate current will flow. A depletion region will form over the whole PN junction area and this will be physically greatest at the high field regions between the drain and gate. The existence of the depletion region reduces the effective channel width and thereby increases the channel resistance. An increase in the value of V_{DS} increases the width of the depletion region. This results in a reduction of the channel cross-section and an increase in channel resistance.

Fig. 2.3 N-channel JFET working below saturation.
N-type conducting channel existing between source and drain.
(Only channel depletion regions are shown.)

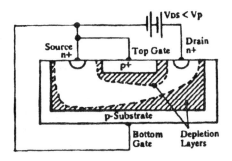

Above a certain V_{DS} value, the channel will no longer exhibit a resistive characteristic but reaches a state of saturation (Fig. 2.4) where the channel current changes very little for a large change in V_{DS}. The JFET is then said to be saturated. This saturation current is given the symbol I_{DSS} which is an abbreviation for the drain-to-source current with the gate short-circuited to the source.

Fig. 2.4 N-channel JFET working in saturation region.
N-channel is almost cut off between drain and source.
(Only channel depletion regions are shown.)

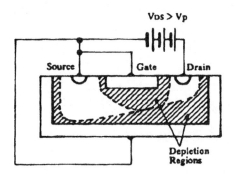

The I_D/V_{DS} characteristic at $V_{GS} = 0V$ is shown in Figure 2.5. Initially I_D increases almost linearly with V_{DS} until the depletion region begins to "pinch-off" the channel, and the curve flattens out at the I_{DSS} value. The value of V_{DS} at which this takes place is termed the "pinch-off" voltage and is given the symbol: Vp.

Fig. 2.5 JFET output characteristic for $V_{GS} = 0V$.

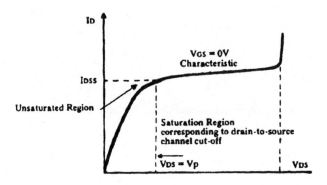

Consider the case of Figure 2.6, where $V_{DS} = 0V$ and a negative gate-source voltage (-V_{GS}) is applied. The depletion region is controlled mainly by the gate-source voltage V_{GS}: the depletion region widens as V_{GS} becomes more negative and consequently the channel resistance increases. Therefore, for values of V_{DS} at or near to zero volts, the drain-source resistance is controlled by V_{GS}. As V_{GS} increases, the channel resistance increases until a voltage $V_{GS(off)}$ is reached, at which level the channel is completely "pinched-off" and no drain current is allowed to flow. This value of $V_{GS(off)}$ is equal in magnitude but opposite in polarity to Vp, and is usually referred to as the "Gate Pinch-off Voltage." It also is given the symbol: Vp.

Fig. 2.6 N-channel JFET showing channel depletion layer when drain-source voltage $V_{DS} = 0V$ and $V_{GS} =$ negative voltage.

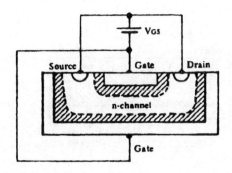

A combination of V_{DS} and V_{GS} bias conditions results in a family of characteristics (Fig. 2.7). From this it is seen that there are two important modes of operation for a JFET, namely:

- Operation to the *left* of the pinch-off voltage locus. This is known as the unsaturated or triode region where I_D is governed by both V_{DS} and V_{GS}. As will be seen later, the triode region is most important when the JFET is used as an analog switch.
- Operating to the *right* of the pinch-off voltage locus. Here the JFET is in the saturated or pentode region and I_D is controlled almost entirely by V_{GS}. In this region, the JFET is most useful as a voltage amplifier.

Fig. 2.7 Family of output characteristics for an N-channel JFET.

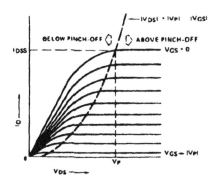

The application of a negative voltage to the gate of an N-channel JFET increases the depth to which the depletion layer extends into the channel, and so reduces the conductivity of the channel. A small positive voltage on the gate has the opposite effect. If the gate-to-channel voltage were sufficient to forward bias the silicon PN junction (approximately 0.6 volts) a significant current would flow from the gate (P-region) into the channel (N-region). For this reason, the N-channel JFET is normally operated with the gate at a negative voltage with respect to the channel. The JFET is therefore considered to be a *depletion-mode* device. The foregoing applies equally to the P-channel JFET except that the voltage polarities are reversed.

JFET Fabrication

Junction FETs are usually manufactured using silicon planar technology. Figures 2.8a-f illustrate the processing steps for fabricating an idealized N-channel JFET.

Fig. 2.8 JFET fabrication steps.

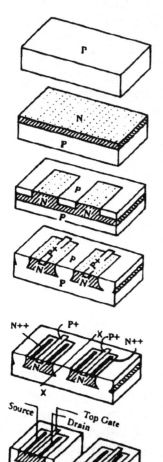

a) P-type silicon wafer (substrate)

b) N-type silicon epitaxial layer grown on to P-type substrate.

c) P-type acceptor impurity diffused in, to start isolation region.

d) P+ impurity diffused in, to form top gate. Simultaneously, P region diffuses to complete isolation between the N islands.

e) N++ type impurity diffused into N-type channel to form Drain and Source contacts. Physical isolation of each JFET is achieved by scribing and breaking wafer along x-x axis

f) Formation of discrete N-channel JFETs after "scribing and breaking" procedure. Since the edges of the P+ regions of the top gate are diffused into the P- substrate, electrical contact is made to the top gate, via the P- substrate.

The process begins with a mono-crystalline substrate of P-type silicon in the form of a circular wafer. A thin layer of N-type silicon is then grown epitaxially on top of the substrate (Fig. 2.8b). The epitaxial process used to form the drain-source channel allows a fine control on dopant concentration and film thickness, important factors if consistent device performance is to be achieved.

A film of silicon dioxide is grown on the surface of the epitaxial layer. A photo-resistive material is applied to the oxide and the wafer is subsequently exposed to ultra-violet light through a mask. Chemical solutions are then used to etch away the unexposed photo-resist and then the silicon dioxide. The photoresist that remains is then removed. An acceptor type impurity is diffused through the pattern in the oxide mask (Fig. 2.8c) to begin the formation of the isolation regions. Further oxide films are grown and subsequently selectively etched; another acceptor type diffusion is performed to produce the top P-type gate, and simultaneously complete the isolation of each N-type island on the substrate (Fig. 2.8d). By a similar process, a donor impurity is diffused into the N-type islands to form the N++ drains and sources. Aluminum is then deposited onto the N++ diffusion regions to form the drain and source contacts. In most cases, the gate contact could be made via the substrate (Fig. 2.8f). The majority of devices have drain and source symmetry that allows complete electrical interchange ability of these two terminals. Depending on the type of FET and wafer size, more than 15,000 FETs can be fabricated on one wafer.

Assembly

The same general assembly techniques are applicable to both JFET and MOSFET devices. A typical discrete FET package is a metal can package. A FET die is mounted onto a metal header. The die is eutectically bonded onto the header which is in electrical contact with one of the three external leads. In this instance, the backgate on the FET is used to make contact with the gate lead. The other two leads are embedded in glass that insulates them from each other and the header body. Attached to these leads are aluminum or gold wires to make connections to the source and drain terminals of the die. The metal can is then welded to the header in a dry nitrogen environment to form a hermetic seal.

Other package options are available, including dual-in-line and flat pack types. Encapsulating materials most commonly used are metal-ceramic, plastic, or epoxy resin. Devices are available with a variety of process and screening options in accordance with military, industrial or consumer reliability specifications. Screening for high reliability devices usually includes a burn-in to eliminate infant mortality failures. Each device is tested to major electrical parameters.

JFET Characteristics

ON Resistance

The high OFF-to-ON resistance ratio of junction field-effect transistors makes them ideal components for use in switching applications. Switching applications usually require ON resistances to be as small as possible. The ON resistance of field-effect transistors depends on the concentration and mobility of the charge carriers in the channel and the physical size of the conducting channel. N-channel devices have lower ON resistance than P-channel devices of similar channel dimensions because of the higher carrier mobility in N-type material.

Junction FET ON Resistance

For a junction FET operating in its saturation region, the value of I_D is essentially independent of V_{DS} and the device has a very high dynamic resistance.

For the same JFET operating in the nonsaturated (triode) region, a junction FET behaves as a resistor whose value is dependent upon V_{GS} and V_{DS}. Indeed for very low values of drain-to-source voltage, I_D is almost linear with V_{DS}, for a given V_{GS}. For this reason JFETs are widely used as voltage controlled resistors. Over a wider range of drain-to-source voltage, r_{DS} will also depend on V_{DS}; the I_D/V_{DS} relationship becomes nonlinear as V_{DS} increases. This limits the useful range of V_{DS}. However, techniques exist which employ feedback between drain and gate to reduce the r_{DS} nonlinearity and to extend the dynamic range of V_{DS}.

A junction FET operating under reverse-biased gate-source conditions, exhibits minimum channel resistance r_{DS} when both V_{GS} and V_{DS} are zero. Under these conditions an N-channel FET with a Vp of 5V and an I_{DSS} of 100mA would exhibit an $r_{DS(on)}$ of 25 ohms. Such a JFET would have an active area of about 0.15 square millimeters. To reduce ON resistance, one option is to increase the active area; for example, produce a N-channel JFET that has an ON resistance of less than 2.5 ohms and has an active area on the order of 1 square millimeter.

The channel resistance of JFETs is temperature dependent. This is due to two effects:
- Charge carrier mobility reduces with increasing temperature and so tends to increase channel resistance.
- The width of the gate-to-channel depletion region decreases with increasing temperature, tending to decrease the resistance.

For low values of V_{GS}, the decrease in carrier mobility is the dominant factor and under these conditions junction field-effect transistors exhibit a positive temperature coefficient of resistance of about 0.7% per°C. Refer to Figure 2.9.

Fig. 2.9 ON Resistance vs. Ambient Temperature for a typical N-channel JFET.

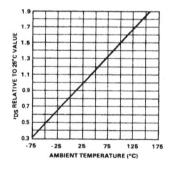

As the gate-source voltage approaches the V$_{GS(off)}$ value, the percentage increase in channel resistance as the temperature increases is balanced by a decrease in resistance due to the decreasing width of the gate-to-channel depletion area. Thus, junction field-effect transistors can be biased to a point at which the resistance has a zero temperature coefficient, as illustrated for a P-channel JFET in Figure 2.10.

Fig. 2.10 r$_{DS}$ vs. V$_{GS}$ and Temperature for a P-channel JFET.

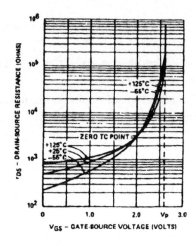

Pinch-Off Voltage (Vp)

The pinch-off voltage, Vp, of a junction field-effect transistor was defined as the drain-to-gate voltage at which the channel begins to "pinch-off." This voltage is largely determined by the depth of the channel and by the impurity concentration in the channel. Junction field-effect transistors of a given geometry are manufactured to various Vp ranges by controlling the depth of the gate diffusion into the channel.

A knowledge of Vp is important since most of the other parameters may be predicted from it. In particular, both I$_{DSS}$ and r$_{DS(on)}$ are functions of Vp. The expression "begins to pinch-off" is an inexact definition and it becomes difficult to specify and test for Vp as a drain-to-gate voltage. For this reason, JFET data sheets specify V$_{GS(off)}$ which has the same magnitude but opposite polarity to the pinch-off voltage. V$_{GS(off)}$ is the gate-to-source voltage required to turn off the JFET and is specified for a particular value of drain voltage and current. Figure 2.11 shows the values of I$_{DSS}$ and r$_{DS(on)}$ plotted against V$_{GS(off)}$ for a typical N-channel JFET geometry.

Fig. 2.11 r_{DS} and I_{DSS} vs. $V_{GS(off)}$ for an N-channel JFET geometry.

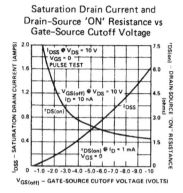

Measurements show that I_{DSS} is approximately proportional to $(Vp)^{1.5}$ and that r_{DS} is approximately proportional to $(Vp)^{-0.5}$.

Pinch-off voltage shows a slight increase with temperature. The voltage Vp consists of the pinch-off potential between gate and channel and the junction barrier potential. Pinch-off potential is constant with temperature, its value being determined by the charge carrier concentration and the square of the channel depth. The junction barrier potential decreases by about 2.2 mV/°C, so Vp will increase at the same rate.

Isolation
Both MOS and junction FETs exhibit extremely high OFF resistance. For most FETs this is greater than 10^{10} ohms and in some FETs can exceed 10^{13} ohms. In FET applications, the leakage currents $I_{S(off)}$ and $I_{D(off)}$ are a better measure of the OFF performance of a switch.

Junction FET Leakage Currents
With an N-channel JFET in the OFF state, the total drain current $I_{D(off)}$ is the sum of the drain-gate junction leakage I_{DG}, and the current $I_{DS(off)}$ flowing to the source through the high resistance of the OFF channel. The resistance comprises that of the depletion region, shunted by the package header resistance. Most metal-can headers have pin-to-pin resistances of greater than 3×10^{13} ohms and the FET depletion region resistance can be in excess of 10^{13} ohms. $I_{DS(off)}$ in most applications is therefore just a few picoamps.

Rule of thumb is that leakage current doubles for approximately every 10°C rise in temperature. In practice, the leakage current increases at a slightly lower rate, as indicated by the graph of Figure 2.11 which shows the gate-to-channel leakage currents I$_{GSS}$ and I$_{D(off)}$ versus temperature for a typical N-channel JFET switch.

Fig. 2.12 Leakage Current vs. Ambient Temperature for a N-channel JFET.

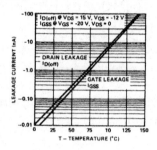

Junction FETs are available with specified maximum OFF leakages ranging from nanoamps to less than one picoamp at 25°C. This wide range is due to the variation in the geometry and processing of different types. Low leakage FETs usually have the smallest geometry.

Offset Voltage

Unlike the bipolar transistor which exhibits a significant V$_{CE}$ offset voltage, the V$_{DS}$ offset for a FET in the ON state is usually negligible. All bipolar transistors have inherent potential barriers at the base-emitter and the base-collector junctions and these must be offset by a small V$_{CE}$ voltage before conduction can occur. This offset voltage is rarely less than 10 millivolts making bipolar transistors unsuitable for switching applications involving low-voltage analog signals.

FET offset voltage results from thermoelectric EMFs generated between source and drain, also from the product of the gate leakage current and the ON resistance. In most applications, these are negligible.

The sources of thermoelectric EMFs for a FET are shown in Figure 2.13. They are from the gold-plated leads in contact with aluminum bonding wires attached to the silicon chip. A temperature gradient of T1-T2 develops between drain and source through localized heating on the chip or through heat applied from external sources via the leads.

Fig. 2.13 Sources of thermoelectric EMFs for a FET.

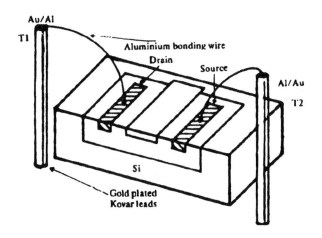

The total thermal offset voltage will be:
(Gold/Aluminum TC + Aluminum/Silicon TC) x (T1 - T2).

The thermoelectric coefficient (TC) for the aluminum-silicon junction is about 0.4 millivolts /°C, while for the gold-aluminum junction it is much less at 0.004 millivolts /°C. If it is assumed that the package leads are at constant temperature, any contribution from the gold junction can be eliminated. Hence, the thermoelectric offset for FETs is about 0.4 mV/°C.

Usually for discrete FETs, due to the small size of the chip and symmetry in the drain-source layout, the T1 and T2 temperatures are nearly equal and the thermoelectric offset is very small; on the order of a few microvolts.

On a large integrated circuit, some parts of the chip will dissipate more heat than others. It is therefore imperative when designing the layout to ensure that drain and source are both in areas which are subjected to the same amount of local heating. Thermoelectric EMFs also exist in bipolar transistors but these are negligible compared with the barrier offset.

The offset voltage resulting from gate leakage current for an N-channel JFET is illustrated in Figure 2.14.

Fig. 2.14 Gate leakage current adds to the drain source offset voltage for an N-channel JFET.

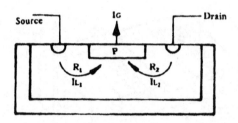

The gate leakage, I_G, comprises leakage currents from the source and drain. These leakage currents flow to the gate via sections of the channel with bulk resistances. At room temperature, this voltage will be extremely small, of the order of 1 nanovolt but since leakage currents increase with temperature, this offset voltage can be several microvolts at 150°C. A similar situation exists with MOSFETs, although the leakage is now from the source and drain to the substrate.

FET Capacitances

All PN junctions exhibit a value of capacitance which is dependent upon the area and depth of the depletion region. For field-effect transistors there is a distributed capacitance between the gate and the channel whose value is determined by the FET geometry, the dopant levels, and the applied voltages. The gate-to-channel capacitance can be considered as two lumped capacitors; the gate-to-source capacitance (C_{gs}) and the gate-to-drain capacitance (C_{gd}). There is also a drain-to-source capacitance (C_{ds}) which is largely the header capacitance but this is small (< 1.0 picoFarads) compared with the others and can usually be neglected.

The junction capacitances are shunted by reverse-biased junction resistances, rgs and rgd. These resistances are of such high values that for most purposes they may be ignored and the gate impedance is considered as purely capacitive.

Most FET data sheets quote junction capacitances with relation to input and output, that is, Ciss and Cirr. The input capacitance, Ciss, is defined as the capacitance between gate and source when the drain is AC short-circuited to the source. Analysis of Figure 2.15 shows that Ciss is defined by the equation: Ciss = Cgs + Cgd.

Fig. 2.15 JFET equivalent circuit.

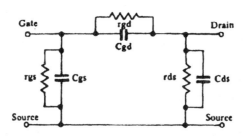

The output capacitance Coss is the capacitance measured between drain and source with the gate shorted to the source. Thus Coss is given by equation: Coss = Cds + Cgd.

If Cds is « Cgd, then Coss ≅ Cgd ≅ Crss. An alternative symbol for Cgd is Crss which refers to the "reverse" capacitance and is usually quoted in data sheets in preference to Cgd or Coss.

For a PN step junction, the capacitance is inversely proportional to the square root of the applied voltage and the variations of Ciss and Crss for a typical N-channel JFET are given in Figure 2.16.

Fig. 2.16 Common Source Capacitances vs. Gate-Source Voltage for a typical N-channel JFET.

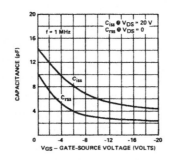

Junction capacitance varies only slightly with temperature, there being a slight increase with increasing temperature due to a decrease in the junction barrier potential. The barrier potential varies by about -2.2 millivolts per °C. Thus, as V_{GS} increases, the temperature dependence becomes less pronounced. The physical size of the FET is a major factor in determining the value of its junction capacitances. The typical curves given in Figure 2.16 relate to a JFET which has an active area of about 0.15 square millimeters. The curves indicate a maximum Ciss of 12 picoFarads. For an N-channel JFET which has an active area of about 1 square millimeter, the typical maximum value of Ciss is 160 picoFarads.

In switching applications the inner-electrode capacitances should be kept as small as possible to minimize charge feed-through of the gate signal into the channel. Since the channel turn-on switching time is largely determined by the gate capacitance, a low value of inner-electrode capacitance is therefore required for fast switching times. Low capacitance is generally achieved by using smaller geometry FETs. This usually implies that the value of ON resistance is likely to increase. The following table of N-channel JFETs illustrates the compromise which must be made between capacitance and r_{DS}.

Device	rDS(ON)	Ciss max.	Crss max.
A	5 ohms	30pF	15pF
B	30 ohms	14pF	3.5pF
C	220 ohms	6pF	1.5pF

Direct comparisons of the respective switching speeds are difficult to make because they are defined for specific circuit configurations and for specific values of load resistance values.

Saturation Current - I_{DSS}
A knowledge of the maximum drain current that a FET can conduct is important in analog switch applications. Ideally, an analog switch should have constant ON resistance over the full signal range, so that for normal purposes the drain current should be considerably less than the saturation drain current. Also, in applications involving sample-and-hold circuits, the capacitor charging rate can be affected by the I_{DSS} value. The drain saturation current of an N-channel JFET varies with gate-source voltage for a given Vp and I_{DSS}; this is illustrated graphically in Fig. 2.17.

Fig. 2.17 Drain Current vs. Gate-Source Voltage for a typical N-channel JFET.

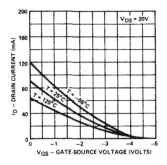

It can be seen in Figure 2.17 that I_{DSS} falls considerably with increasing temperature. This is due to a reduction in the channel carrier mobility. Junction FETs are available with I_{DSS} values ranging from a few milliamps to over 1 amp.

Breakdown Voltage

The maximum analog signal which may be switched is limited by the gate-to-channel breakdown voltage or the drain-to-source breakdown voltage. In junction field-effect transistors, breakdown results from avalanche multiplication of carriers in the depletion region. On JFET data sheets this breakdown voltage is given the symbol BV_{GSS}, that is, the breakdown between gate and source with the source and drain electrically short-circuited. Typical gate-to-channel breakdown voltages for junction field-effect transistors are in the range 30-100 volts. However, avalanche breakdown between the channel and the body restricts the maximum drain-to-source voltage.

Application Information

The JFET enjoys certain inherent advantages over bipolar transistors because of the unique construction and method of operation of the field-effect device. These characteristics include:

- High gain
- Low noise
- Low leakage
- Fast switching
- No thermal runaway
- Zero temperature coefficient Q-point
- Very high dynamic range (> 100db)
- High input impedance at low frequencies
- Junction capacitance independent of device current
- Low distortion and negligible intermodulation products.

The input impedance of a FET is simply the impedance of a reverse-biased PN junction, which is on the order of 10^{10} to 10^{12} ohms. In practice, the input impedance is limited by the value of the shunt gate resistor used in a self-bias common-source circuit configuration. At RF frequencies, the input impedance drop is proportional to the square of the frequency. Also, the input susceptance increases linearly with frequency, since it is a simple parasitic capacitance.

The FET has very high dynamic range, in excess of 100db. Thus, it can amplify very small signals because it produces very little noise, or it can amplify very large signals because it has negligible intermodulation distortion products. It also has a zero temperature coefficient bias point (zero TC point) at which changes in temperature do not change the quiescent operating point.

Junction field-effect transistor capacitances are more constant over wide current variation than are the same parameters in a bipolar device. This inherent stability allows high-frequency (VHF through L-band) oscillators to be built which are far more stable than oscillators using low-frequency crystals and multiplier stages.

FET Terminology and Parameters

Any introduction to the nature, behavior, and applications of field-effect transistors requires that certain questions be answered on FET electrical quantities and parameters; in particular, the most important parameters, and the means by which they can be measured. The following discussion will define specific FET parameters and their associated subscript notations.

Major parameters include:
- C_{gd} - Gate-drain capacitance
- C_{gs} - Gate-source capacitance
- $V_{GS(off)}$ - Gate-source cutoff voltage
- g_{fs} - Common-source forward transconductance
- I_{DSS} - Drain current with the gate shorted to the source
- I_{GSS} - Gate-to-source current with the drain shorted to the source
- $V_{(BR)GSS}$ - Gate-to-source breakdown voltage with the drain shorted to the source.

Special attention should be given to the subscript "s" because it has two different meanings and three possible uses. In FET notations, an "s" for the first or second subscript identifies the source terminal as a node point for voltage reference or current flow. However, when using triple subscript notation, an "s" for the third subscript does not refer to the FET source terminal. It is an abbreviation for "shorted," and signifies that all terminals not designated by the first two subscripts must be tied together and shorted to the common terminal, which is always the second subscript. Therefore, the term I_{GSS} refers to the gate-source current with the drain tied to the source.

Junction Field-Effect Transistors (JFETs)

Junction Field-Effect Transistors (JFETs) are available in both N-channel and P-channel polarities. Symbols are shown in Figure 2.18. Junction FETs, a majority carrier device, have no minority carrier storage time with a low drain-source ON resistance.

Fig. 2.18 JFET circuit symbols.

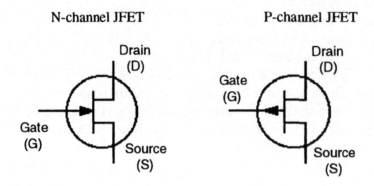

General circuit applications include:
- Interface
- Switching
- Amplification.

The P-channel or N-channel JFET switch is a depletion-mode device. To maintain it in the ON-state, the value of V_{GS} should be at or near zero volts. To implement the ON-state, the gate-and-source or gate-and-drain can be connected together through a resistor, or the gate-to-channel diode can be slightly forward-biased by the leakage current of a diode placed in the gate circuit. In either case, the V_{GS} will remain at or near zero volts for all DC levels of analog signal. Consequently, the resistance of the FET is kept constant and equal to $r_{DS(on)}$ for all values of analog signal.

The following list of applications indicates the versatility of the JFET:

- **Current Limiters**
- **Mixers**
- **Voltage-Controlled Resistors**
- **Amplifiers**
  DC
  Selectivity
  High Gain
  Low Noise
  Small Signal
  Low Distortion
  High Frequency
- **Oscillators**
- **Protection Diodes**
  Low Leakage
- **Switches**
  Analog Gate
  Chopper-Type
  Communicator

JFET Biasing Techniques

Engineers who are not familiar with proper biasing methods often design FET amplifiers that are unnecessarily sensitive to device characteristics.

One way to obtain consistent circuit performance, in spite of device variations, is to use a combination of constant-voltage and self-biasing. The combined circuit configuration turns out to be the same as that generally used with bipolar transistors, but its operation and design are quite different.

For certain JFET applications, such as high-frequency amplifiers, an asymmetrical geometry is preferred for lower capacitance and improved frequency response. In these cases, the source and drain leads should not be interchanged.

Three basic common-source circuits can be used to establish a FETs operating point (Q-point). The Q-point is established by the intersection of the load line and the V_{GS} output characteristic. The three basic biasing schemes are:

- **Constant-voltage bias**, is most useful for RF and video amplifiers employing small DC drain resistors.
- **Constant-current bias**, which is best suited to low-drift DC amplifier applications such as source followers and source-coupled differential pairs.
- **Self-bias** (also called source bias or automatic bias), is particularly valuable for AC amplifiers.

N-Channel JFETs

JFETs have maintained their popularity over the years because they offer exceptional features: low noise, low leakage, high gain, and fast switching. These features that even today cannot be matched by integrated circuits or bipolar transistors.

Unlike the bipolar transistor, which requires a base-drive current, a field-effect transistor is operated by the application of a gate voltage. Thus, while the bipolar transistor exhibits low-input impedance, the JFET offers just the opposite; a very high-impedance gate.

The high-impedance nature of a JFET means superb low-leakage qualities; often specified in the low picoamp range. When this is coupled with good frequency response, JFETs ensure minimal circuit loading for such sensitive applications as sample-and-hold circuits and input devices for operational amplifiers.

An additional and fundamental advantage of the JFET is its extraordinary low noise; so low that in comparative studies with bipolar transistors, the JFET is considered noiseless! This advantage is most obvious in applications involving high source impedances, such as those needed for low-noise electronic and capacitor microphone amplifier circuits.

To meet a wide range of "problem solving" applications, manufacturers offer a broad selection of N-channel amplifiers and switches designed and specified to meet the most stringent circuit requirements. For super high input impedance requirements, device offerings include 1pA maximum leakage, while other series typicals are in the 1 to 5pA range. For critical switching applications, guaranteed ON-resistance as low as 3 ohms coupled with picoamps of leakage and 5 to 15ns typical switching speeds are available. Other devices focus on low-voltage operation down to 1.5V. For broad-band, high-frequency requirements, devices are available for 450MHz and above applications combining high gain with extremely low noise and distortion.

P-Channel JFETs

P-channel JFETs are ideal for high-side switching applications and combine excellent off-isolation with very fast switching. As a complement to N-channel JFETs, the P-channel JFET includes amplifiers and switches specified for a wide range of voltage and current requirements. Several devices are specified for low-voltage and battery-powered applications.

Monolithic and Matched N-Channel JFET Duals

Monolithic and matched N-channel JFET duals offer the designer a wide range of device choices to "stretch" performance in critical circuit designs. Using a specialized discrete dual JFET in front of a low-cost BiFET op amp, such circuits can achieve all the benefits of extreme low noise, low leakage, and high slew rate/wideband performance. Several duals are manufactured with computer matching of die pairs to minimize the parasitic capacitance and inductance that degrade high-frequency performance.

Popular applications for JFET duals include:
- High-speed comparators
- Wideband differential amplifiers
- Ultra low-noise differential amplifiers
- Matched switches/voltage variable resistors
- High-speed temperature compensated single-ended amplifiers.

To serve this wide range of applications, several duals have been specified for ultra low leakage requirements, extraordinarily low noise, high gain and high speed, and low offset/drift voltage.

JFETs as Voltage-Controlled Resistors (VCRs)

A Voltage-Controlled Resistor (VCR) may be defined as a three-terminal variable resistor where the resistance value between two of the terminals is controlled by a voltage potential applied to the third.

Voltage-controller resistors provide a predictable, nearly ohmic-variable resistor controlled by voltage variations on the high-impedance device gate. The device uses mid-range $V_{GS(off)}$ limits to maximize the dynamic range.

Key applications benefiting from the voltage-controlled resistance variation and high drive impedance include:
- Attenuators
- Servo motors
- Phase shifters
- Op-amp adjustable gain control.

For a junction field-effect transistor under certain operating conditions, the resistance of the drain-source channel is a function of the gate-source voltage alone and the JFET will behave as an almost pure ohmic resistor. Maximum drain-source current, I_{DSS}, and minimum resistance $r_{DS(on)}$, will exist when the gate-source voltage is equal to zero volts ($V_{GS} = 0$). If the gate voltage is increased (negatively for N-channel JFETs and positively for P-channel), the resistance will also increase. When the drain current is reduced to a point where the FET is no longer conductive, the maximum resistance is reached. The voltage at this point is referred to as the pinch-off or cut-off voltage, and is symbolized by $V_{GS} = V_{GS(off)}$. Thus, the device functions as a voltage-controlled resistor.

Most amplification or switching operations of FETs occur in the constant-current (saturated) region. A close inspection of the unsaturated or pre-pinch-off area reveals that the effective slope indicative of conductance across the channel from drain-to-source is different for each value of gate-source bias voltage. The slope is relatively constant over a range of applied drain voltages, so long as the gate voltage is also constant and the drain voltage is low.

The unique resistance-controlling properties of FETs can be deduced from the output characteristics. All pass through the origin, near which they become almost straight lines so that the incremental value of channel resistance, r_{DS}, is essentially the same as that of DC resistance, r_{DS}, and is a function of V_{GS}.

While such devices are normally operated with a positive drain-source voltage, small negative values of V_{DS} are possible. This is because the gate-channel PN junction must be slightly forward-biased before any significant amount of gate current flows. A device with a channel of small cross-sectional area will exhibit a high $r_{DS(on)}$ and a low I_{DSS}. Thus a FET with high I_{DSS} should be chosen when design requirements indicate the need for a low $r_{DS(on)}$.

DMOS FETs

DMOS FETs feature sub-nanosecond switching speeds and near gigahertz amplifier capabilities. DMOS FETs bridge the performance gap between conventional FETs and gallium arsenide (GaAs) devices. Products are available as single and quad array switch types.

DMOS products are fabricated using a silicon-gate double-diffused MOS process to offer the ultimate in low-cost, yet highly reliable switches. The unique construction affords all the benefits critical to amplification and small-signal switching applications.

The benefits are:
- Good off-isolation
- Ultrafast switching speed
- High operating frequency
- Exceptionally low capacitance
- Absence of shunt D-S diode permits large analog signal switching.

Key applications which benefit from this technology include:
- Video switching
- Precision sample-and-hold applications
- Operating frequencies beyond 450MHz
- Any high-performance application which benefits from sub-nanosecond turn-on time and sub-picofarad capacitance.

Chapter 3

MOSFETs

The Metal Oxide Semiconductor Field-Effect Transistor (MOSFET) uses a film of high purity dielectric such as silicon dioxide or silicon nitride to insulate the gate from the channel. Due to the insulation properties of the MOS gate, both positive and negative gate voltages may be applied to unprotected MOSFETs.

In early MOSFETs, the formation of an N-channel relied upon the charge induced by the oxide impurities at the oxide-semiconductor interface. The repeatability, therefore, was not good. Present day MOSFETs are fabricated by a much cleaner and repeatable process. The introduction of an additional N-type region between N+ type source and drain forms the initial channel. This is enhanced or depleted according to the gate voltage applied.

In operation, a negative gate voltage must be applied to turn the channel OFF and in this sense the device behaves exactly as an N-channel JFET. However, if a positive voltage is applied to the gate, additional negative charges will be attracted to the oxide/semiconductor interface thus increasing the channel conductivity. The device can therefore be operated in both depletion and enhancement mode.

Four forms of MOSFETs are possible:
- N-Channel Depletion
- N-Channel Enhancement
- P-Channel Depletion
- P-Channel Enhancement

Depletion MOSFETs

Figure 3.1 shows the basic cross-section of an N-channel depletion-mode MOSFET.

Fig. 3.1 Idealized cross-section through an N-channel depletion-mode MOSFET.

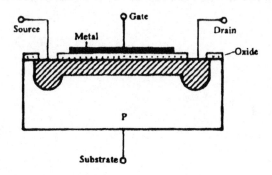

Figure 3.2 shows the family of output characteristics for a typical N-channel depletion MOSFET.

Fig. 3.2 Family of output characteristics for an N-channel depletion MOSFET.

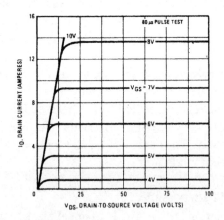

The symbols for depletion MOSFETs are shown in Figure 3.3.

Fig. 3.3 Symbols for depletion MOSFETs.

N-channel depletion MOSFET   P-channel depletion MOSFET

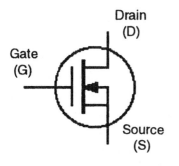
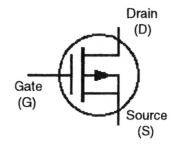

Enhancement MOSFETs

Enhancement MOSFETs are normally OFF devices requiring the application of either a negative (for P-channel MOS) or positive (for N-channel MOS) gate voltage before channel conduction is possible. The operation of a P-channel enhancement MOSFET is illustrated in Figures. 3.4 to 3.6.

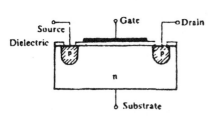

Fig. 3.4 Idealized cross-section through a P-channel enhancement MOSFET showing negative charge region existing at the oxide/semiconductor interface with no gate voltage applied.

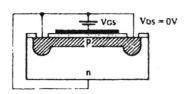

Fig. 3.5 Showing induced P-channel when $V_{GS} \gg V_{GS(th)}$ ($V_{DS} = 0V$).

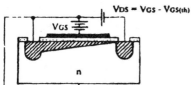

Fig. 3.6 Showing the pinch-off of the P-channel as drain voltage increases negatively with respect to the substrate.

The device consists of an N-type substrate into which a P-type impurity is diffused to form separate sources and drains. The metal gate is insulated from the substrate by an oxide layer. As in the depletion MOSFET, free electrons are inherently attracted to the oxide/semiconductor interface to form an N-type layer, which has a higher concentration of negative charge carriers than the surrounding N-type substrate shown in Figure 3.4. When the gate-to-source voltage is zero, virtually no current can flow from source to drain or from drain to source as there is a reverse-biased junction in each direction. Therefore, the device is normally OFF. If a negative gate-to-source voltage is applied, the built-in potential barrier between the source and the channel region is decreased electrostatically. When the gate source voltage reaches a value called "threshold voltage," the source and channel junction barrier beneath the gate oxide disappears. Any further increase in gate voltage produces a P-type layer beneath the gate thus forming a conducting channel between the source and drain (Fig. 3.5) whose conductivity increases with increasing V_{GS}. If a negative drain voltage is applied with respect to the source, the drain-gate differential voltage will now be reduced and consequently the channel narrows toward the drain. When $V_{DS}-V_{GS} = V_{GS(th)}$ the channel will be pinched-off at the drain (Fig. 3.6).

Any further increase in V_{DS} would have little effect on the value of the channel unless V_{GS} were increased, this would then require a greater V_{DS} for the pinch-off current. Figure 3.7 shows a family of output characteristics for a typical P-channel enhancement MOSFET.

Fig. 3.7 Family of output characteristics for a P-channel enhancement MOSFET.

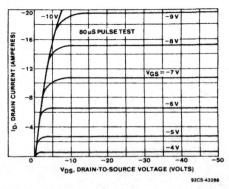

The design and operation of an N-channel enhancement MOSFET is similar to the P-channel enhancement MOS but voltage polarities are reversed. The circuit symbols are shown in Figure 3.8.

Fig. 3.8 Symbols for enhancement MOSFETs.

N-channel enhancement MOSFET   P-channel enhancement MOSFET

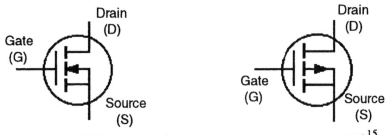

The extremely high gate-to-channel resistances in excess of 10^{15} ohms present a problem when handling MOSFETs. Electro-static charge build-up at the gate can cause the gate-channel capacitance to charge up to voltages which can be in excess of the gate-to-channel dielectric breakdown. Permanent damage to the dielectric can therefore occur. To protect the gate dielectric, many MOSFETs are manufactured with an integrated zener clamp, which consists of a PN junction, between the gate and substrate. The zener breakdown voltage is designed to be less than that of the gate dielectric but sufficiently high to prevent limitation of the operating voltage. Since the zener diode is reverse-biased during normal operation, the gate leakage current is almost completely determined by the diode leakage current. Dielectric leakage current is a minor factor in comparison. A *protected* MOSFET has inherently a much higher gate leakage current than an unprotected MOSFET.

MOSFET ON-Resistance
The high OFF-to-ON resistance ratio of field-effect transistors makes them ideal components for use in switching applications. Switching applications usually require ON resistances to be as small as possible. The ON resistance of field-effect transistors depends on the concentration and mobility of the charge carriers in the channel and the physical size of the conducting channel. N-channel devices have lower ON resistance than P-channel devices of similar channel dimensions because of the higher carrier mobility in N-type material.

Since the MOSFET has an extremely thin induced channel, it tends to have a higher ON resistance than a JFET of similar size. Even so, the geometry of a conventional P-channel MOSFET can be tailored to give very low ON resistance.

When a MOSFET is operated well into the saturation region, i.e., $|V_{DS}| > |V_{GS}| - |V_{GS(tb)}|$, V_{DS} has little effect and I_D is almost entirely controlled by V_{GS}.

In the unsaturated (triode) region, as with JFETs, the r_{DS} of a MOSFET is dependent not only on V_{GS} but also upon V_{DS}, the minimum ON resistance occurring when $|V_{GS} - V_{DS}|$ is a maximum. Therefore, if MOS devices are used in switching circuits that have fixed gate voltages applied in the ON state, the channel resistance will be modulated by any variation in the analog signal voltage.

Clearly for P-channel devices, the minimum ON resistance is achieved when the analog signal is at its most positive value. Figure 3.9 shows that the resistance can vary by a factor of 3:1 over the analog range -10V to +10V. Figure 3.9 illustrates how r_{DS} varies with analog signal for a typical P-channel enhancement MOSFET.

Fig. 3.9 r_{DS} vs. V_D for a P-channel enhancement MOSFET.

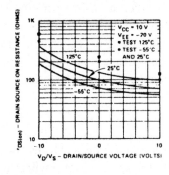

For those applications in which the variation in r_{DS} is unacceptably high, a JFET having a constant ON resistance over the analog range, would be more suitable than a MOSFET. Alternatively, a designer could use N-channel and P-channel MOSFETs connected in parallel. A negative going analog signal which causes an increase in the r_{DS} of the P-channel MOS simultaneously causes a decrease in the r_{DS} of the N-channel MOS. Such complementary MOSFET arrangements are used extensively in integrated circuits.

The effects of temperature on channel resistance are similar in both MOS-FETs and JFETs. An increase in temperature causes a reduction in the channel carrier mobility, and a reduction in the threshold voltage. The net effect is that MOSFET channel resistance exhibits a positive temperature coefficient of about 0.4% /°C for high values of V_{GS}. This coefficient falls with V_{GS} until a zero temperature coefficient point is reached as shown in Figure 3.10.

Fig. 3.10 $r_{DS(on)}$ vs. V_{GS} and Temperature for a P-channel MOSFET.

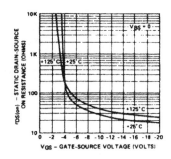

Isolation

Both MOSFETs and JFETs exhibit extremely high OFF resistance. For most FETs this is greater than 10^{10} ohms and in some FETs can exceed 10^{15} ohms. In FET applications, the leakage currents $I_{S(off)}$ and $I_{D(off)}$ are a better measure of the OFF performance of a switch.

MOSFET Leakage Currents

The extremely high gate-to-channel resistance isolates any direct leakage paths from the channel into the gate. However, leakage paths exist from the source and drain (also from the gate in protected devices) into the substrate via the reverse-biased junctions (Fig. 3.11). The leakage values are of the same order as those for JFETs and have similar characteristics although the OFF leakages $I_{S(off)}$ and $I_{D(off)}$ show a greater dependence upon V_{DS}.

Fig. 3.11 Equivalent circuit of a P-channel protected MOSFET showing the OFF leakage paths.

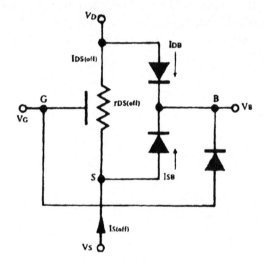

Offset Voltage

The gate leakage I_G, comprises leakage currents from the source and drain. These leakage currents flow to the gate via sections of the channel with bulk resistances. At room temperature, this voltage will be extremely small, on the order of 1 nanovolt, but since leakage currents increase with temperature, this offset voltage can be several microvolts at 150°C. A similar situation exists with MOSFETs, although the leakage is now from the source and drain to the substrate.

MOSFET Capacitances

As mentioned in the JFET chapter, most FET data sheets quote junction capacitances with relation to input and output, that is, Ciss and Crss. The input capacitance, Ciss, is defined as the capacitance between gate and source when the drain is AC short-circuited to the source. The output capacitance, Coss is the capacitance measured between drain and source with the gate shorted to the source.

In the case of MOSFETs, channel-to-body junction capacitance must also be considered. This can be treated in a similar manner to the gate capacitance of a JFET. For simplicity, this is considered as two lumped capacitances C_{db} and C_{sb}. Figure 3.12 shows the variation of C_{db} and C_{sb} for a typical P-channel enhancement MOSFET.

Fig. 3.12 Typical substrate capacitance vs. Voltage for a P-channel enhancement MOSFET.

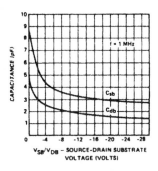

MOS gate capacitance is a minimum when the device is OFF. When the device turns ON, the carrier concentration in the channel increases with a subsequent increase in gate-channel capacitance. Figure 3.13 illustrates the sharp increase in Cgs and Cgd that occur when the gate-source voltage is close to $V_{GS(th)}$ for an enhancement MOSFET.

Fig. 3.13 Typical Gate Capacitance vs. Voltage for a P-channel enhancement MOSFET.

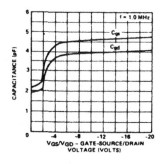

Threshold Voltage - $V_{GS(th)}$

The threshold voltage of MOS devices depends upon the doping concentration in the interface body or substrate region. Silicon MOS switches with silicon dioxide as the dielectric are manufactured using either high or low threshold processes. The basic difference between the two processes being in the choice of the gate oxide thickness and body or channel doping concentration.

When enhancement MOSFETs are used for analog switching, a low threshold voltage is desirable to minimize the gate voltage excursion is required. Thus, even with the low threshold processes, a minimum V_{GS} of 2 to 3 volts is required to turn the switch ON. This can be a disadvantage for applications involving low analog signals, as considerable errors can be introduced by charge coupling through the gate-channel capacitance. FETs with a low $V_{GS(th)}$ (or Vp) are therefore preferable for such applications. The substrate bias has a considerable effect on the value of $V_{GS(th)}$, if the substrate channel junction reverse bias is increased, a higher gate voltage is required to maintain conduction. Refer to Figure 3.14.

Fig. 3.14 Gate Threshold Voltage vs. Substrate Bias for a
P-channel enhancement MOSFET.

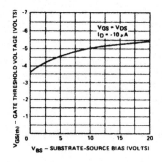

Increasing temperature causes a reduction in $V_{GS(th)}$ by about 4 mV/°C for the high threshold process and about 2.7 mV/°C for low threshold devices. In addition, if the manufacturing process is not clean, a significant shift in $V_{GS(th)}$ can occur if the device is operated at high temperatures for any length of time. This shift is the result of a migration of impurity ions in the oxide which occurs at elevated temperature and under the influence of applied voltages. When the device returns to a normal working temperature the redistribution of charges in the gate oxide results in a change of threshold voltage. The impurities are normally positively charged sodium ions so that if the gate is maintained at a negative voltage and at high temperature, the ions will be attracted away from the oxide/semiconductor interface with a consequent reduction in threshold voltage. The magnitude of the shift in $V_{GS(th)}$ due to this mechanism depends on time, temperature, impurity concentration and gate bias voltage.

Saturation Current - I_{DSS}

A knowledge of the maximum drain current that a FET can conduct is important in analog switch applications. Ideally, an analog switch should have constant ON resistance over the full signal range, so that for normal purposes the drain current should be considerably less than the saturation drain current. Also, in applications involving sample-and-hold circuits the capacitor charging rate can be affected by the I_{DSS} value. For MOSFETs, a typical example of the drain saturation current is illustrated in Figure 3.15.

Fig. 3.15 Drain Saturation Current vs. V_{GS} for a typical P-channel enhancement MOSFET.

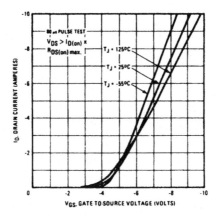

Since MOSFETs can operate in the enhancement mode, the maximum drain saturation current is usually limited by the maximum power dissipation or gate breakdown voltages of the device.

Breakdown Voltage

The maximum analog signal which may be switched is limited by the gate-to-channel breakdown voltage or the drain-to-source breakdown voltage. The gate dielectric of MOSFETs usually has a breakdown voltage in the range of 7 to 100 volts depending on the gate oxide thickness. However, avalanche breakdown between the channel and body restricts the maximum drain-to-source voltage. The minimum drain-to-source breakdown, BV_{DSS}, for small signal planar MOSFETs is usually on the order of 30 volts. For high breakdown geometries, BV_{DSS} can reach several hundred volts.

For "protected" MOSFETs, the maximum analog signal is also limited by the breakdown voltage of the gate-to-body diode BV_{GBS}. If this value is exceeded by the analog-to-gate voltage, current will flow from the channel into the gate via the substrate.

Application Information

MOSFETs are well suited for low-voltage battery operated, space-limited applications, and are ideal devices for load switching and efficient power switching in:

- Pagers
- PCS handsets
- Cellular phones
- Notebook computers
- Low-current/low-voltage applications.

MOSFET advantages are:

- Simpler drive circuitry
- The ability to be paralleled
- Significantly faster switching times
- The absence of a second-breakdown failure mechanism
- Stable gain and response time over a wide temperature range.

Fig. 3.16 MOSFET symbols.

N-channel depletion mode

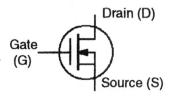

P-channel depletion mode

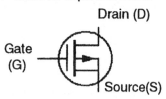

N-channel enhancement mode

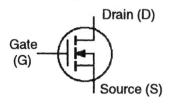

P-channel enhancement mode

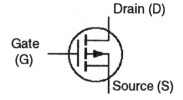

Dual gate N-channel depletion mode

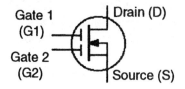

Dual gate N-channel enhancement

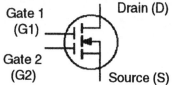

To maintain an N-channel or P-channel MOSFET switch in the ON-state, the gate is usually held at some reference voltage which ensures that the V_{GS} exceeds the threshold voltage of the MOSFET, even when the analog signal (V_A) is at the extremes of its dynamic range, hence keeping the MOSFET on for all values of V_A. However, since the r_{DS} of a MOSFET is related to V_{GS}, the r_{DS} will vary as the analog signal voltage level varies.

The variation in ON resistance on the transistor with analog signal is a serious limitation in some applications since it can cause distortion of the analog output signal. This can be minimized if the load resistance is high compared with the switch resistance.

Metal oxide semiconductor field-effect transistors differ from bipolar transistors in operating principles, specifications, and performance. In fact, the performance characteristics of MOSFETs are generally superior to those of bipolar transistors.

There are some fundamental performance differences between MOSFETs and JFETs. JFETs, by nature, operate only in the depletion mode. That is, a reverse gate bias depletes, or pinches off the flow of channel current. A MOSFET, by virtue of its electrically-insulated gate, can be fabricated to perform as either a depletion-mode or enhancement-mode FET. The enhancement-mode MOSFET offers no channel between the source and drain.

Quite unlike the JFET, a depletion-mode MOSFET will also perform as an enhancement-mode FET. MOSFETs can assume several forms and operate in either the depletion/enhancement-mode or enhancement-mode only.

A MOSFET has a metal oxide coating between gate and channel. The oxide insulates the gate from the channel. As a result, the MOSFET has very high input resistance, higher than the JFET. As with the JFET, the gate controls the main or channel current. The gate-source voltage can be positive or negative. This would not be possible with a JFET.

The MOSFET is also available in an enhancement-only mode where a gate signal only enduces or enhances channel current; the gate signal never depletes the channel current. There are P-channel enhancement MOSFETs, where a negative gate voltage enhances channel conductivity and N-channel enhancement mode MOSFETs where a positive gate voltage enhances channel conductivity.

Breakdown voltage in MOS devices do not depend upon PN junction stress but rather upon the thickness and quality of the insulating oxide. When breakdown does occur, the oxide is punctured and the device is destroyed.

By virtue of its electrically-isolated gate, a MOSFET is described as a high-input impedance, voltage-controlled device. Whereas a bipolar transistor is a low-input-impedance, current-controlled device. As a majority-carrier semiconductor, a MOSFET stores no charge, and so can switch faster than a bipolar device. Majority-carrier semiconductors also tend to slow down as temperature increases. This effect, brought about by another phenomenon called carrier mobility (where mobility is a term that defines the average velocity of a carrier in terms of the electrical field imposed on it) makes a MOSFET more resistive at elevated temperatures, and much more immune to the thermal-runaway problem experienced by bipolar devices.

A useful by-product of the MOSFET process is the internal parasitic diode formed between source and drain. (There is no equivalent for this diode in a bipolar transistor other than in a bipolar Darlington transistor.) Its characteristics make it useful as a clamp diode in inductive-load switching.

MOSFET operation is the creation of the inversion channel beneath the gate when an electric charge is applied to the gate. Because of the MOSFETs construction, an integral diode is formed on the device, and the designer can use this diode for a number of circuit functions.

Power MOSFETs

A power MOSFET is a voltage-driven device whose gate terminal is electrically isolated from its silicon body by a thin layer of silicon dioxide (SiO_2); (bipolar transistors are current-driven). As a majority-carrier semiconductor, the MOSFET operates at much higher speed than its bipolar counterpart because there is no charge-storage mechanism; (bipolar is a minority-carrier). A positive voltage applied to the gate of an N-type MOSFET creates an electric field in the channel region beneath the gate; that is, the electric charge on the gate causes the P-region beneath the gate to convert to an N-type region. This conversion, called the surface-inversion phenomenon, allows current to flow between the drain and source through an N-type material. In effect, the MOSFET ceases to be an NPN device when in this state. The region between the drain and source can be represented as a resistor, although it does not behave linearly, as a conventional resistor would. Because of this surface-inversion phenomenon, then, the operation of a MOSFET is entirely different from that of a bipolar transistor, which always retains its NPN characteristic.

Power MOSFETs are manufactured using a vertical double diffused process, called VDMOS or simply DMOS. A DMOS MOSFET is a single silicon chip structured with a large number of closely packed hexagonal or square cells. The number of cells varies according to the dimensions of the chip. For example, a 120-mil^2 chip contains about 5,000 cells; a 240-mil^2 chip has more than 25,000 cells.

Most DMOS processes develop the polysilicon gate structure rather than the older metal-gate type. If the resistance of the gate structure is high, the switching time of the DMOS device is increased, thereby reducing its upper operating frequency. Compared to a metal gate, a polysilicon gate has a higher gate resistance. This property accounts for the frequent use of metal-gate MOSFETs in high-frequency (greater than 20MHz) applications, and polysilicon-gate MOSFETs in higher-power but lower-frequency systems.

MOSFETs do not have hot-spotting because their current flow is in the form of majority carriers. The mobility of majority carriers (where, again, mobility is a term that defines the average velocity of a carrier in terms of the electrical field imposed on it) is temperature dependent in silicon: mobility decreases with increasing temperature. This inverse relationship dictates that the carriers slow down as the chip gets hotter. In effect, the resistance of the silicon path is increased, which prevents the concentrations of current that lead to hot spots. In fact, if hot spots do attempt to form in a MOSFET, the local resistance increases and defocuses or spreads out the current, rerouting it to cooler portions of the chip.

Because of the character of its current flow, a MOSFET has a positive temperature coefficient of resistance. The positive temperature coefficient of resistance means that a MOSFET is inherently stable with temperature fluctuation, and provides its own protection against thermal runaway and secondary breakdown. Another benefit of this characteristic is that MOSFETs can be operated in parallel without fear that one device will rob current from the others. If any device begins to overheat, its resistance will increase, and its current will be directed away to cooler chips.

To permit the flow of drain-to-source current in an N-type MOSFET, a positive voltage must be applied between the gate and source terminals. Since, as described above, the gate is electrically isolated from the body of the device, theoretically no current can flow from the driving source into the gate. In reality, however, a very small current, in the range of tens of nanoamperes, does flow, and is identified on data sheets as a leakage current, I_{GSS}. Because the gate current is so small, the input impedance of a MOSFET is extremely high (in the megohm range) and, in fact, is largely capacitive rather than resistive (because of the isolation of the gate terminal).

The MOSFET's switching speed is determined by its input resistance (R), and its input capacitance (C_{ISS}). The elements are equivalent, rather than physical, resistance, R, and capacitance, C. The capacitance, called C_{ISS} on MOSFET data sheets, is a combination of the device's internal gate-to-source and gate-to-drain capacitance. The resistance, R, represents the resistance of the material in the gate circuit. Together, the equivalent R and C of the input circuit determine the upper frequency limit of MOSFET operation.

Since the frequency response of a MOSFET is controlled by the effective resistance (R) and capacitance (C) of its gate terminal, a rough estimate can be made of the upper operating frequency from datasheet parameters. The resistive portion depends on the sheet resistance of the polysilicon-gate overlay structure. But whereas the total R value is not found on datasheets, the C value (C_{ISS}) is; it is recorded as both a maximum value and in graphical form as a function of drain-to-source voltage. The value of C_{ISS} is closely related to chip size; the larger the chip, the greater the value. Since the RC combination of the input circuit must be charged and discharged by the driving circuit, and since the capacitance dominates, larger chips will have slower switching times than smaller chips, and are, therefore, more useful in lower-frequency circuits. In general, the upper frequency limit of most power MOSFETs spans a fairly broad range from 1MHz to 10MHz.

Probably the most used MOSFET graphical data is the output characteristics or plot of drain-to-source voltage (V_{DS}) as a function of drain-to-source current (I_D). A typical characteristic gives the drain current that flows at various V_{DS} values as a function of the gate-to-source voltage (V_{GS}). The curve is divided into two regions: a linear region in which V_{DS} is small and drain current increases linearly with drain voltage, and a saturated region in which increasing drain voltage has no effect on drain current (the device acts as a constant-current source). The current level at which the linear portion of the curve joins with the saturated portion is called the "pinch-off" region.

Summary

When considering the V_{GS} level required to operate a MOSFET, the device is not turned on (no drain current flows) unless V_{GS} is greater than a certain level (called the threshold voltage). In other words, the threshold voltage must be exceeded before an appreciable increase in drain current can be expected. Generally, V_{GS} for many types of DMOS devices is at least 2V. This is an important consideration when selecting devices or designing circuits to drive a MOSFET gate: the gate-drive circuit must provide at least the threshold-voltage level, but preferably a much higher one.

A MOSFET must be driven by a fairly high voltage, on the order of 10V, to ensure maximum saturated drain-current flow. However, integrated circuits, such as TTL types, cannot deliver the necessary voltage levels unless they are modified with external pull-up resistors. Even with a pull-up to 5V, a TTL driver cannot fully saturate most MOSFETs. Thus, TTL drivers are most suitable when the current to be switched is far less than the rated current of the MOSFET. CMOS ICs can run from supplies of 10V, and these devices are capable of driving a MOSFET into full saturation. On the other hand, a CMOS driver will not switch the MOSFET gate circuit as fast as a TTL driver. The best results, whether TTL or CMOS ICs provide the drive, are achieved when special buffering chips are inserted between the IC output and gate input to match the needs of the MOSFET gate.

Low-Voltage Power MOSFETs

Low-voltage power MOSFETs are fabricated by a process yielding a wide range of both N-channel and P-channel enhancement-mode and N-channel depletion-mode devices. Some types can be operated directly from integrated circuits.

This structure allows:
- Low capacitance
- Low on-resistance
- Fast switching times
- A high-impedance gate
- High breakdown voltage
- High current handling capability
- Freedom from the thermal runaway effect common to bipolar devices.

To serve a wide range of applications, low-power MOSFETs features N-channel enhancement-mode devices. P-channel devices are designed to complement N-channel products. High-side switching is one application for which these devices are ideal.

Logic Level Power MOSFET applications include:
- Solenoid drivers
- Automotive switching
- Programmable controllers.

As the demand for lower power supply voltages and smaller device size increases, the standard MOSFET flat P-body/N-epi junction technology has process and design limitations. In order to decrease the package size and the power dissipation, Vishay Siliconix developed a technology to increase cell density by placing the gate electrode of a power DMOSFET into a narrow trench (compared to the gate width of conventional DMOSFET) that is etched vertically from the surface and insulated by gate oxide. By adding more cells in the same area basically cuts the resistance of the channel when it is fully enhanced by the gate-to-source voltage.

Increased cell density provides:
- Reduced on-resistance
- Lower gate-drive voltage
- Lower parasitic capacitances.

These features lead to higher efficiency and faster switching rates. Higher switching rates cut the size of a switcher's inductors and capacitors and increases their response time. This tiny die also makes it possible to manufacture multichip power ICs with additional features.

These low-voltage power MOSFETs are designed for:
- High and low-side switching.
- Buck and Boost switching regulators, including synchronous switchers.
- Battery Disconnect Switches (BDS) - Safety switches for Li-Ion batteries.

High-Voltage MOSFETs

High-voltage, N-channel depletion-mode devices feature normally ON operation, breakdown voltages over 200V, and a specified low ON-resistance. Depletion-mode performance makes these devices an excellent choice for telecommunications and industrial process control applications. However, majority of the high-voltage power MOSFETs are enhancement-mode N-channel devices which operate in a normally OFF mode.

Applications include:
- Relay drivers
- Motor drivers
- Switching regulators
- Switching converters
- Drivers (emitter switches) for high-power bipolar switching transistors requiring high speed and low gate-drive power.

Some power MOSFETs are specially designed to withstand a specified level of energy in the breakdown avalanche mode of operation.

Parallel operated MOSFETs must have the V_{th} ratings very, very close to each other. Otherwise, the device with the low V_{th} will carry most of the current especially during the switch. A mismatch can even blow-up the device with the lower V_{th}.

Logic level power MOSFETs are specifically designed for use with logic level (5V) driving sources. This performance is accomplished through a special gate oxide design which provides full rated conduction at gate biases in the 3V-5V range, therefore facilitating true ON-OFF power control directly from logic circuit supply voltages.

P-Channel MOSFETs used for High-Side Switching

Historically, P-channel FETs were not considered as useful as their N-channel counterparts. The higher resistivity of P-type silicon, resulting from its lower carrier mobility, put it at a disadvantage compared to N-type silicon.

Getting N-type performance out of P-type FETs has meant larger area geometries with correspondingly higher interelectrode capacitances. Consequently, a truly complementary pair; a P-channel and an N-channel device that match in all parameters; is impossible.

Yet, despite its shortcomings, the P-channel MOSFET performs a vital "high-side" switch task that the N-channel simply cannot equal.

Used as a high-side switch, a P-channel MOSFET in a totem-pole arrangement with an N-channel MOSFET will simulate a high-current. high-power CMOS (Complementary MOS) arrangement. Although the P-channel MOSFET cannot complement the N-channel in both ON-resistance and capacitance simultaneously, such combinations as a low-threshold P-channel and the N-channel together offer outstanding performance as a complementary pair.

The principal application of the P-channel, enhancement-mode FET is in switching power (or voltage) to grounded (ground return) loads.

To drive the FET properly, the gate voltage must be referenced to its source. For enhancement-mode MOSFETs, this gate potential is of the same polarity as the MOSFET's drain voltage. To turn ON the N-channel MOSFET requires a *positive* gate-source voltage, whereas the P-channel MOSFET requires a *negative* gate-source potential.

During switching, a MOSFET's source voltage must remain fixed, as any variation will modulate the gate and thus adversely affect performance.

Glossary

Semiconductor Definitions

Absolute maximum ratings
The values specified for "ratings," "maximum ratings," or "absolute maximum ratings" are based on the "absolute system" and unless otherwise required for a specific test method are not to be exceeded under any service or test conditions. These ratings are limiting values beyond which the serviceability of any individual semiconductor device may be impaired. Unless otherwise specified, the voltage, current, and power ratings are based on continuous DC power conditions at free air ambient temperature of +25°C. For pulsed or other conditions of operation of similar nature, the current, voltage, and power dissipation ratings are a function of time and duty cycle. In order not to exceed absolute ratings, the equipment designer has the responsibility of determining an average design value, for each rating, below the absolute value of that rating by a safety factor, so that the absolute values will never be exceeded under any usual conditions of supply-voltage variation, load variation, or manufacturing variation in the equipment itself.

Ambient temperature
Ambient temperature is the air temperature measured below a semiconductor device, in an environment of substantially uniform temperature, cooled only by natural air convection and not materially affected by reflective and radiant surfaces.

Anode
The electrode from which the forward current flows within the device.

Blocking
A term describing the state of a semiconductor device or junction which eventually prevents the flow of current.

Breakdown voltage
The breakdown voltage is the maximum instantaneous voltage, including repetitive and nonrepetitive transients, which can be applied across a junction in the reverse direction without an external means (circuit) of limiting the current. It is also the instantaneous value of reverse voltage at which a transition commences from a region of high small-signal impedance to a region of substantially lower small-signal impedance.

Case mount
A type of package (outline) which provides a method of readily attaching one surface of the semiconductor device to a heat dissipater to achieve thermal management of the case temperature (examples: TO-3, DO-4, etc.).

Case temperature
Case temperature is that temperature measured at a specified point on the case of a semiconductor device.

Cathode
The electrode to which the forward current flows within the device.

Characteristic
An inherent and measurable property of a device. Such a property may be electrical, mechanical, thermal, hydraulic, electromagnetic, or nuclear, and can be expressed as a value for stated or recognized conditions. A characteristic may also be a set of related values usually shown in graphical form.

Constant current source
A current source shall be considered constant if halving the generator impedance does not produce a change in the parameter being measured that is greater than the required precision of the measurement.

Constant voltage source
A voltage source shall be considered constant if doubling the generator impedance does not produce a change in the parameter being measured that is greater than the required precision of the measurement.

Disc type
A type of package (outline) for very high power devices which provides two parallel surfaces for mounting into a specialized heat dissipator capable of applying a specified compressive force to the device.

Forward bias
The bias which tends to produce current flow in the forward direction (P-type semiconductor region at a positive potential relative to N-type region).

Impulse duration
The time required for an impulse waveform to decay to 50 percent of the peak value measured from the start of the virtual front duration of zero crossover.

Impulse waveform
A pulse with a defined virtual front and impulse duration for either a voltage or current amplitude of unidirectional polarity.

Noise figure
At a selected input frequency, the noise figure is the *ratio* of the total noise power per unit bandwidth (at a corresponding output frequency) delivered to the output termination; *to* the portion thereof contributed at the input frequency by the input termination whose noise temperature is standard (293°K) at all frequencies.

Open circuit
A circuit shall be considered as open circuited if halving the magnitude of the terminating impedance does not produce a change in the parameter being measured greater than the specified accuracy of the measurement.

Package type
A package type is a package which has the same case outline, configuration, materials (including bonding, wire, or ribbon and die attach), piece parts (excluding preforms which differ only in size), and assembly processes.

Passivation
A grown oxide.

Pulse
A pulse is a flow of electrical energy of short duration.

Pulse average time
The average pulse time of a pulse is the time duration from a point on the leading edge which is 50 percent of the maximum amplitude to a point on the trailing edge which is 50 percent of the maximum amplitude.

Pulse delay time
The delay time of a pulse is the time interval from a point at which the leading edge of the input pulse has risen to 10 percent of its maximum amplitude to a point at which the leading edge of the output pulse has risen to 10 percent of its maximum amplitude.

Pulse fall time
The fall time of a pulse is that time duration during which the amplitude of its trailing edge is decreasing from 90 to 10 percent of the maximum amplitude.

Pulse rise time
The rise time of a pulse is that time duration during which the amplitude of its leading edge is increasing from 10 to 90 percent of the maximum amplitude.

Pulse storage time
The storage time of a pulse is the time interval from a point 10 percent down from the maximum amplitude on the trailing edge of the input pulse to a point 10 percent down from the maximum amplitude on the trailing edge of the output pulse.

Pulse time
The time of a pulse is the interval from the point on the leading edge which is 90 percent of the maximum amplitude *to* the point on the trailing edge which is 90 percent of the maximum amplitude.

Radiation failures
A radiation failure is defined at the lowest radiation level when either any device parameter exceeds its specified Post Irradiation Parameter Limits (PIPL) or the device fails any functional test in accordance with stated test conditions.

Radiation Hardness Assurance (RHA)
That portion of performance verification testing that assures that parts meet the radiation response characteristics as specified in this specification and the performance specification sheet.

Rating
The nominal value of any electrical, thermal, mechanical, or environmental quantity assigned to define the operating conditions under which a component, machine, apparatus, or electronic device is expected to give satisfactory service.

Reverse bias
The bias which tends to produce current flow in the reverse direction (N-type semiconductor region at a positive potential relative to the P-type region).

Semiconductor devices
Electronic device in which the characteristic distinguishing electronic conduction takes place within a semiconductor.

Semiconductor diode
A semiconductor device having two terminals and exhibiting a nonlinear voltage-current characteristic.

Semiconductor junction
A region of transition between semiconductor regions of different electrical properties (e.g., N-N+, PN, P-P+ semiconductors) or between a metal and a semiconductor.

Short circuit
A circuit shall be considered short-circuited if doubling the magnitude of the terminating impedance does not produce a change in the parameter being measured that is greater than the specified accuracy of the measurement.

Small signal
A signal shall be considered small if doubling its magnitude does not produce a change in the parameter being measured that is greater than the specified accuracy of the measurement.

Storage temperature
Storage temperature is a temperature at which the device may be stored without any power being applied.

Temperature coefficient
The ratio of the change in a parameter to the change in temperature.

Thermal compression bond
A bond achieved when pressure and temperature are present regardless of how the temperature rise was achieved except without ultrasonic assist.

Thermal equilibrium
Thermal equilibrium is reached when doubling the test time interval does not produce a change, due to thermal effects, in the parameter being measured that is greater than the specified accuracy of the measurement.

Thermal resistance
Thermal resistance is the temperature rise, per unit power dissipation, of a junction above the temperature of a stated external reference point under conditions of thermal equilibrium.

Thyristor
A bistable semiconductor device that comprises three or more junctions and can be switched from the "off" state or "on" state to the opposite state.

Transistor
An active semiconductor device capable of providing power amplification and having three or more terminals.

Virtual front duration
The pulse time as defined by 1.67 times time for voltage to increase from 30 percent to 90 percent of crest (peak value) or 1.25 times time for current to increase from 10 percent to 90 percent of crest.

Semiconductor symbols

F	Noise figure
R_θ	Thermal resistance
$R_{\theta CA}$	Thermal resistance, case to ambient
$R_{\theta JA}$	Thermal resistance, junction to ambient
$R_{\theta JC}$	Thermal resistance, junction to case
$R_{\theta JL}$	Thermal resistance, junction to lead
$R_{\theta JR}$	Thermal resistance, junction to reference
T_A	Ambient or free air temperature
T_C	Case temperature
TEC	End cap temperature
T_j	Junction temperature
TL	Lead temperature
T_{op}	Operating temperature
T_{STG}	Storage temperature
t_d	Delay time
t_f	Fall time

t_{off} .... Turn-off time

t_{on} .... Turn-on time

t_p .... Pulse time

t_r .... Rise time

t_s .... Storage time

t_w .... Pulse average time

$V_{(BR)}$ .... Breakdown voltage

Note: Symbology may vary amoung manufacturers. The symbols used in this section are listed in the military standard for the general performance specifications of semiconductor devices (Mil-Prf 19500L).

Transistor definitions

For junction transistors and multijunction types.

Base
A region which lies between an emitter and collector of a transistor and into which minority carriers are injected.

Collector
A region through which a primaly flow of charge carriers leaves the base.

Cutoff current
The cutoff current is the measured value of DC current when a transistor is reverse-biased by a voltage less than the breakdown voltage.

Emitter
A region from which charge carriers that are minority carriers in the base are injected into the base.

Junction. collector
A semiconductor junction, normally biased in the reverse direction, the current through which can be controlled by the introduction of minority carriers into the base.

Junction, emitter
A semiconductor junction normally biased in the forward direction to inject minority carriers into the base.

Saturation
A base current and a collector current condition resulting in a forward-biased collector junction.

Transistor symbols

Junction transistors and multijunction type symbols.

C_{ibo}, C_{ieo} .... Input capacitance, (common base, common emitter) collector open circuited for AC

C_{ibs}, C_{ies} .... Input capacitance, (common base, common emitter) collector short-circuited to reference terminal for AC

C_{obo}, C_{oeo} .... Output capacitance, (common base, common emitter) input open-circuited to AC

C_{obs}, C_{oes} .... Output capacitance, (common base, common emitter) input short-circuited to reference for AC

f_{hfb}, f_{hfc}, f_h .... Small signal, short-circuit forward current transfer ration cutoff frequency (common base, common collector, common emitter)

f_{max} .... Maximum frequency of oscillation

f_T .... Extrapolated unity gain frequency

g_{MB}, g_{MC}, g_{ME} .... Static transconductance (common base, common collector, common emitter)

g_{mb}, g_{mc}, g_{me} .... Small signal transconductance (common base, common collector, common emitter)

G_{PB}, G_{PC}, G_{PE} ... . Large signal insertion power gain (common base, common collector, common emitter)

G_{pb}, G_{pc}, G_{pe} .... Small signal insertion power gain (common base, common collector, common emitter)

h_{FB}, h_{FC}, h_{FE} .... Static forward current transfer ratio (common base, common collector, common emitter)

h_{fb}, h_{fc}, h_{fe} .... Small signal short-circuit forward current transfer ratio (common base, common collector, common emitter)

$|h_{fe}|$ .... Magnitude of common emitter small signal short circuit forward current transfer ratio.

h_{IB}, h_{IC}, h_{IE} .... Static input resistance (common base, common collector, common emitter)

h_{ib}, h_{ic}, h_{ie} .... Small signal short circuit input impedance (common base, common collector, common emitter)

h_{ob}, h_{oc}, h_{oe}	Small signal open circuit output admittance (common base, common collector, common emitter)
h_{rb}, h_{rc}, h_{re}	Small signal open circuit reverse voltage transfer ratio (common base, common collector, common emitter)
I_B	Base current (DC)
I_C	Collector current (DC)
I_E	Emitter current (DC)
i_B	Base current (instantaneous total value)
i_C	Collector current (instantaneous total value)
i_E	Emitter current (instantaneous total value)
I_{CBO}	Collector cutoff current (DC) emitter open
I_{CEO}	Collector cutoff current (DC) base open
I_{CER}	Collector cutoff current (DC) with specified resistance between base and emitter

I_{CES} .... Collector cutoff current (DC) base short circuited to emitter

I_{CEV} .... Collector cutoff current (DC) with specified voltage between base and emitter

I_{CEX} .... Collector cutoff current (DC) with specified circuit between base and emitter

I_{EBO} .... Emitter cutoff current (DC) collector open

I_{ECS} .... Emitter cutoff current (DC) base short-circuited to collector

I_S .... Collector efficiency

P_C .... Collector power dissipation

P_T .... Total power dissipation, all terminals

R_B .... External base resistance

r_b .... Base spreading resistance

rb'cc .... Collector-base time constant

R_C .... External collector resistance

$r_{CE(sat)}$ .... Collector to emitter saturation resistance

R_E .... External emitter resistance

r_{iep}	Small signal short circuit parallel input resistance (common emitter)
t_c	tOFF crossover time (the time interval during which the collector voltage decreases from 10 percent of its peak off-state value and the collector current decreases to 10 percent of its peak on state value)
V_{BB}	Base supply voltage
V_{BE}	Base to emitter voltage (DC)
$V_{BE(sat)}$	Base to emitter saturation voltage
$V_{(BR)CBO}$	Breakdown voltage collector to base, emitter open
$V_{(BR)CEO}$	Breakdown voltage collector to emitter, base open V~BR)CER voltage collector to emitter, with specified resistance between base and emitter
$V_{(BR)CER}$	Breakdown voltage collector to emitter, with specified resistance between base and emitter
$V_{(BR)CES}$	Breakdown voltage collector to emitter, with base short-circuited to emitter

$V_{(BR)CEX}$ .... Breakdown voltage collector to emitter, with specified circuit between base and emitter

$V_{(BR)EBO}$ .... Breakdown voltage emitter to base, collector open

V_{CB} .... Collector to base voltage (DC)

V_{CBF} .... DC open circuit voltage (floating potential) between the collector and base, with the emitter biased in the reverse direction with respect to the base

V_{CBO} .... Collector to base voltage (static), emitter open

V_{CC} .... Collector supply voltage

V_{CE} .... Collector to emitter voltage (DC)

V_{ce} .... Collector to emitter voltage (rms)

v_{ce} .... Collector to emitter voltage (instantaneous)

$V_{CE(Sat)}$ .... Collector to emitter saturation voltage

V_{CEO} .... Collector to emitter voltage (static) base open

$V_{CEO(sus)}$ .... Breakdown voltage, collector to emitter, sustained

V_{CER} .... Collector to emitter voltage (DC), with specified resistance between base and emitter

V_{CES} .... Collector to emitter voltage (DC), base short-circuited to emitter

V_{EB} .... Emitter to base voltage (DC)

V_{eb} .... Emitter to base voltage (rms)

V_{eb} .... Emitter to base voltage (instantaneous)

V_{EBF} .... DC open circuit voltage (floating potential) between the emitter and base, with the collector biased in the reverse direction with respect to the base

$V_{(BR)CEV}$ .... Breakdown voltage collector to emitter, with specified voltage between base and emitter

V_{EBO} .... Emitter to base voltage (static) collector open

V_{EC} .... Emitter to collector voltage (DC)

V_{ECF} .... DC open circuit voltage (floating potential) between the emitter and collector, with the base biased in the reverse direction with respect to the collector

V_{EE} .... Emitter supply voltage

V_{RT} .... Reach through voltage

Unijunction transistor definitions

Peak point
The point on the emitter current-voltage characteristic corresponding to the lowest current at which the change in emitter base voltage with respect to emitter current equals zero.

Unijunction transistor
A three-terminal semiconductor device having one junction and a stable negative-resistance characteristic over a wide temperature range.

Valley point
The point on the emitter current-voltage characteristic corresponding to the second lowest current at which the change in emitter base voltage with respect to emitter current equals zero.

Unijunction transistor symbols

$I_{B2(mod)}$ .... Interbase modulated current

I_{EB20} .... Emitter reverse current

I_p .... Peak point current

I_v .... Valley point current

r_{BB} .... Interbase resistance

V_{B2B1} .... Interbase voltage

$V_{EB1(sat)}$ .... Emitter saturation voltage

V_{OB1} .... Base - 1 peak voltage

V_p .... Peak point voltage

V_v .... Valley point voltage

h .... Intrinsic standoff ratio

FET definitions

Depletion-mode operation
The operation of a FET such that changing the gate to source voltage from zero to a finite value decreases the magnitude of the drain current.

Depletion-type FET
A FET having appreciable channel conductivity for zero gate to source voltage. The channel conductivity may be increased or decreased according to the polarity of the applied gate to source voltage.

Drain
A region into which majority carriers flow from the channel.

Enhancement-mode operation
The operation of a FET such that changing the gate to source voltage from zero to a finite value increases the magnitude of the drain current.

Enhancement-mode FET
A FET having substantially zero channel conductivity for zero gate to source voltage. The channel conductivity may be increased by the application of a gate to source voltage of appropriate polarity.

FET - Field-Effect Transistor
A transistor in which the conduction is due entirely to the flow of majority carriers through a conduction channel controlled by an electric field arising from a voltage applied between the gate and source terminals.

Gate
The electrode associated with the region in which the electric field due to the control voltage is effective.

Insulated-gate FET
A FET having one or more gate electrodes which are electrically insulated from the channel.

Junction-gate FET
A FET that uses one or more gate regions to form PN junction(s) with the channel.

MOSFET - Metal Oxide Semiconductor Field-Effect Transistor
An insulated gate FET in which the insulating layer between each gate electrode and the channel is oxide material.

N-channel FET
A FET that has an N-type conduction channel.

P-channel FET
A FET that has a P-type conduction channel.

Source
A region from which majority carriers flow into the channel.

FET symbols

b_{is}	Small-signal, common-source, short-circuit, input susceptance
b_{os}	Small-signal, common-source, short-circuit, output susceptance
b_{fs}	Small-signal, common-source, short-circuit, fonnlard transfer susceptance
b_{rs}	Small-signal, common-source, short-circuit, reverse transfer susceptance
C_{ds}	Small-signal, drain to source capacitance
C_{du}	Small-signal, drain to substrate capacitance
C_{iss}	Small-signal, common-source, short-circuit, input capacitance

C_{oss}	Small-signal, common-source, short-circuit, output capacitance
C_{rss}	Small-signal, common-source, short-circuit, reverse transfer capacitance
D,d	Drain terminal
E_{AR}	Repetitive avalanche energy capability
E_{AS}	Single pulse avalanche energy capability
G,g	Gate terminal
g_{fs}	Small-signal, common-source, short-circuit, forward transfer conductance
g_{is}	Small-signal, common-source, short-circuit, input conductance
g_{os}	Small-signal, common-source, short-circuit, output conductance
G_{pg}	Small-signal, common-gate insertion power gain
G_{ps}	Small-signal, common-source insertion power gain
g_{rs}	Small-signal, common-source, short-circuit, reverse transfer conductance

G_{tg} .... Small-signal, common-gate, transducer power gain

G_{ts} .... Small-signal, common-source transducer power gain

I_D .... Drain current

I_{AR} .... Rated avalanche current (repetitive and nonrepetitive)

$I_{D(on)}$ .... On-state drain current

$I_{D(off)}$ .... Drain cutoff current

I_{DSS} .... Zero-gate-voltage drain current

I_G .... Gate current

I_{GF} .... Forward gate current

I_{GR} .... Reverse gate current

I_{GSS} .... Reverse gate current with all other terminals short-circuited to source (junction-gate)

I_{GSSF} .... Forward gate current with all other terminals short-circuited to source (insulated-gate)

I_{GSSR} .... Reverse gate current with all otherterminals short-circuited to source (insulated-gate)

I_S .... Source current through drain diode (forward biased V_{SD})

$I_{S(off)}$ .... Source cutoff current

I_{SDS} .... Zero-gate-voltage source current

$I_{(ISO)}$ .... Source pin to case isolation current

$Q_{g(th)}$ .... Gate charge that must be supplied to reach minimum specified gate-source threshold voltage

$Q_{g(on)}$ .... Gate charge that must be supplied to reach the gate-source voltage specified for the device

$Q_{gm(on)}$ .... Gate charge that must be supplied to the device to reach the maximum rated gate-source voltage

Q_{gs} .... Charge required by C_{GS} to reach a specified I_D

Q_{gd} .... Charge supplied to the drain from the gate to change the drain voltage under constant drain current conditions

$r_{ds(on)}$ .... Small-signal drain to source on-state resistance

$r_{DS(on)}$	Static drain to source on-state resistance
S,s	Source terminal
$t_{d(off)}$	Turn-off delay time
$t_{d(on)}$	Turn-on delay time
U, u	Substrate (bulk) (terminal, when substrate is externally terminated)
$V_{(BR)GSS}$	Gate to source breakdown voltage, all other terminals short-circuited to source (junction-gate)
$V_{(BR)DSS}$	Drain to source breakdown voltage, all other terminals short-circuited to source (junction-gate)
$V_{(BR)GSSF}$	Forward gate to source breakdown voltage
$V_{(BR)GSSR}$	Reverse gate to source breakdown voltage
V_{DD}	Drain supply voltage
V_{DG}	Drain to gate voltage
V_{DS}	Drain to source voltage
$V_{DS(on)}$	On-state drain to source voltage

V_{DU} .... Drain to substrate voltage

V_{GG} .... Gate supply voltage

V_{GP} .... Gate plateau voltage

V_{GS} .... Gate to source voltage

V_{GSF} .... Forward gate to source voltage

V_{GSR} .... Reverse gate to source voltage

$V_{GS(off)}$ .... Gate to source cutoff voltage

$V_{GS(th)}$ .... Gate to source threshold voltage

V_{GU} .... Gate to substrate voltage

V_{ISO} .... Source pin to case isolation voltage

V_{SS} .... Source supply voltage

V_{SU} .... Source to substrate voltage

y_{fs} .... Magnitude of small-signal common-source short-circuit forward transfer admittance

y_{is} .... Magnitude of small-signal common-source short-circuit input admittance

y_{rs} .... Magnitude of small-signal common-source short-circuit reverse transfer admittance

Bibliography

Many thanks to the following who gave permission to use their information for reference, or for incorporation nto this book:

General Semiconductor, Inc., Melville, NY 11747: *Small Signal Transistors, Schottky Diodes and Switching Diodes* Databook (Printed 9/98).

Harris Semiconductor, Melbourne, FL 32902: *Power MOSFETs*, 1994 Databook; *MCT/IGBTs/Diodes*, 1995 Databook.

Rohm Electronics U.S.A., Antioch, TN 37013: *Transistors '97-'98* DataBook.

Vishay Intertechnology, Inc., Malvern, PA 19355:
Vishay Siliconix: *Analog Switches;* 1980 Databook,
             Small Siganl FET Design Catalog, July 1983.
Vishay Telefunken (formerly Temic): *Small-Signal Discrete Products*,
             1997 Databook.

Additional References:

American Microsemiconductor Inc., Madison NJ 07940.

D.O.D. MIL-PRF-19500L, *Performance Specification Semiconductor Devices, General Specification For*, 22 October 1998.

Appendix A

FET Switches

One of the most common control elements in electrical circuitry is the simple ON-OFF switch. This has evolved over the years from the manually operated circuit breaker of the early experimenters to the multiswitch integrated circuit of today. In every application, the function of the switch remains the same, via. to isolate or connect two sections of an electrical circuit.

Until the advent of the thermionic valve, switching action was effected almost exclusively by the manual or electromechanical opening and closing of metal contacts. The operation of mechanical switches is easily understood and they require a very simple form of maintenance. However, with today's increasing demands of modern circuits, it has become evident that electro-mechanical switches alone cannot meet all requirements and that there are applications in which only electronic types are viable. By far the most popular of these is the semiconductor switch.

In recent years, semiconductor switches have made inroads into application areas that hitherto have been exclusively the domain of electromechanical devices. Solid-state switches are now used in sample-and-hold circuits; multiplexers; high power switching; chopper circuits etc., whereas in the past some form of electromechanical switch would have been used.

Types of FET switches

- *JFET* - The P-channel or N-channel JFET switch is a depletion-mode device. To maintain it in the ON-state, the value of VGS should be at or near zero volts. To implement the ON -state, the gate-and-source or gate-an-drain can be connected together through a resistor, or the gate-to-channel diode can be slightly forward-biased by the leakage current of a diode placed in the gate circuit. In either case, the V_{GS} will remain at or near zero volts for all DC levels of analog signal. Consequently, the resistance of the FET is kept constant and equal to $r_{DS(on)}$ for all values of analog signal.

- *MOSFET* - To maintain an N-channel or P-channel MOSFET switch in the ON-state, the gate is usually held at some reference voltage which ensures that the V_{GS} exceeds the threshold voltage of the MOSFET, even when the analog signal (V_A) is at the extremes of its dynamic range, hence keeping the MOSFET on for all values of VA. However, since the r_{DS} of a MOSFET is related to V_{GS} , the r_{DS} will vary as the analog signal voltage level varies. The variation in ON resistance on the transistor with analog signal is a serious limitation in some applications since it can cause distortion of the analog output signal. This can be minimized if the load resistance is high compared with the switch resistance.

Comparison of Electromechanical and Semiconductor Switches

The types of electromechanical and semiconductor switches available are many and varied, each having some advantages and some disadvantages. The choice between a mechanical and semiconductor switch usually depends upon the application. The performance and major switching parameters of both types are compared in the following pages.

ON Resistance

Most electromechanical switches initially have very low ON-resistance, typically tens of milliohms. During their lifetime, however, wear at the switch contact surfaces can increase this resistance value by a factor of a hundred or more. Semiconductor switches have higher ON resistance but their resistance is constant over the switch lifetime. field-effect transistors are available with ON resistances of less than 2 ohms and some high power bipolar transistors can have collector-emitter saturation resistances of less than 100 milliohms. If the application required a switch with near zero ON resistance, the main contender would then be the electromechanical type, but if a constant ON resistance over the switch lifetime is of prime importance, then the semiconductor switch is far more preferable.

OFF Isolation

The maximum OFF resistance of electromechanical switches is limited by surface conduction along the package. This resistance is reduced considerably in moist environments or through careless handling. Nevertheless, extremely high OFF resistance is possible, and with specially treated reed switches this can be as high as 10^{12} ohms. The OFF resistance of semiconductor switches can have the same order of magnitude. The value of the semiconductor switch leakage current is roughly proportional to the square root of the voltage across the junction, and it increases with increasing temperature. Values of junction leakages can be less than one picoamp at 25°C for low power field-effect transistor switches.

Switching Speed

Semiconductor switches comprise no moving parts, hence their switching speed is not limited by contact inertia. Consequently, switching times of nano-seconds are easily attainable and maximum switching rates are often in excess of 10^6 operations per second. By comparison electromechanical switches are slow indeed. Even the fastest of reed switches have turn-on/turn-off times measured in milliseconds, and maximum switching rates rarely exceed a few hundred operations per second.

Maximum ON Current

Power dissipation ratings limit the maximum currents that semiconductor devices are able to switch: collector currents of up to 100 amperes are possible with bipolars, while the largest field-effect transistors at present have maximum drain currents in the region of 10 amperes. High power switches, with forced cooling, can conduct currents of up to 1000 amperes. Some electromechanical switches are capable of conducting currents of many thousands of amperes, but switching such high currents with these devices causes severe arcing and burning of contact faces. Electromechanical switches capable of conducting thousands of amperes are therefore normally switched when the load current is zero.

Maximum OFF Voltage

For electromechanical switches the maximum OFF voltage is limited by the voltage breakdown of the insulating dielectric. For large switches, with wide contact spacing, the maximum OFF voltage can be many hundreds of thousands of volts. The smaller electromechanical devices, reed switches, miniature relays etc. are capable of switching several hundreds of volts.

Operation of semiconductor switches relies on PN junction action. Consequently the reverse biased breakdown voltage of the junction sets a limit to the maximum voltage that can be switched. Some thyristor devices have breakdown voltages as high as 1000 volts, while bipolar and field-effect transistors can have maximum switching voltages in the region of 200 volts. It must be stressed that this is more than adequate to meet the needs of most semiconductor systems which normally run off supplies of less than 50 volts.

Minimum Analog Voltage

The minimum analog voltage switchable is determined by the total error signal contributed by the switch. One source of error in electromechanical devices is the thermal EMF generated across the moving contacts. This can be tens of microvolts. A much larger error, prevalent in dry reed relays, results from the dynamic noise generated by contact bounce. This can be as high as 500 microvolts peak-to-peak initially, decaying to tens of microvolts after a few milliseconds.

Bipolar semiconductor switches require a finite collector-emitter voltage to maintain conduction. This voltage which is seldom less than a few millivolts, appears as an offset and severely limits the minimum value of analog voltage that can be switched.

Field-effect transistors have no such offset and are used extensively in low voltage switching applications. The thermal EMFs generated in field-effect transistors are virtually zero, owing to their near symmetrical structure. Factors affecting the low level analog switching voltage capability of FETs are switching transient breakthrough into the channel from the gate and thermal noise due to the channel ON resistance.

Drive Signals

Compatibility with existing circuits is an important consideration when deciding on a switch type. If, as is frequently the case, there is some degree of involvement with computers or other electronic systems which require standard logic control signals, then switching systems which respond to the same type of logic signals are desirable. The voltage levels required to operate electromechanical switches normally vary between 1 and 250 volts and most require a driving power greater than 50mW. Since logic driving circuits are limited in their power handling capability, this necessarily means that electromechanical switches usually require some form of interfacing with their logic control elements. Mast semiconductor switches, owing to their lower drive power requirements, are directly compatible with transistor logic systems.

Switching Life

Since electromechanical switches comprise some moving parts, their operating life is affected by mechanical wear; in particular, wear at the contact surfaces. This can lead to an increase in ON resistance and the eventual welding together of the contacts. Figures for operating lifetimes or switching cycles are difficult to assess since they depend on operating conditions. A dry reed relay switching at the rate of 100Hz would perform 10^8 switching operations in only 300 hours which is approximately the minimum expected lifetime of the relay.

This figure would be greatly reduced if the relay were switching into an inductive or capacitive load. Inductive loads produce arcing at the switch contacts because of the back EMF induced when the switch is opened. Capacitive loads accelerate contact wear due to current surges when the switch turns on. The switching life of a semiconductor device is not limited by mechanical wear and provided it is operated within its maximum specified ratings it can continue to switch almost indefinitely. For example, the Mean Time Before Failure (MTBF) of semiconductor devices is usually well in excess of 100,000 hours. Consequently, a semiconductor switch operating at 10^6 Hz could perform in excess of 3.6×10^{14} cycles during its operating life.

Reliability

In many applications the ability of a device to survive in adverse environments is most important. Military and space equipments need to withstand extremes of temperature, pressure, mechanical shock etc. without impairing operation. In general, semiconductor devices exhibit greater resistance to adverse environments than electromechanical types. Semiconductors are less susceptible to damage or change of state through shock, vibrations or high accelerations and do not suffer from sticking contacts due to freezing at very low temperatures. Their electrical characteristics are dependent on temperature and are somewhat prone to change when subjected to high energy radiation. However, this does not prevent their use in military equipment requiring an operating temperature range of -55°C to 125°C, or in satellite applications with the attendant high radiation environment.

System Size

Size, power consumption and weight of components become increasingly important as systems grow more complex. In this respect, the semiconductor switch has distinct advantages over its electromechanical counter part. The use of integrated circuits and modern fabrication techniques enable multiple switches to be contained in a single robust package. For example, one package may have 16 switches with their binary decode circuitry in a 28 pin package measuring only 1.4 inches x 0.6 inches. An equivalent system using relays would be considerably more bulky.

System Costs

Total system costs should take into account not only the initial capital outlay but also factors such as maintenance costs, personnel training and the secondary costs resulting from system failures. Switch for switch, the costs for electromechanical and semiconductor types are comparable, but as circuit complexity increases the cost per switch for semiconductor systems using integrated circuits falls, giving them a considerable price advantage over electromechanical types. Costly equipment down-time is also greatly reduced with semiconductor systems due to their higher reliability and longer lifetimes.

Appendix B

Equations

Metric Prefixes

Pico	$\times 10^{-12}$	Tera	$\times 10^{12}$
Nano	$\times 10^{-9}$	Giga	$\times 10^{9}$
Micro	$\times 10^{-6}$	Mega	$\times 10^{6}$
Milli	$\times 10^{-3}$	Kilo	$\times 10^{3}$
Deci	$\times 10^{-1}$	Deca	$\times 10^{1}$

Symbols

E = Voltage in *Volts*
I = Current in *Amperes*
R = Resistance in *Ohms*
P = Power in *Watts*

C = Capacitance in *Farads*
L = Inductance in *Henries*
X_C = Capacitive Reactance in *Ohms*
X_L = Inductive Reactance in *Ohms*

Basic Formulas

1. Ohm's Law

$$E = IR = \frac{P}{I} = \sqrt{PR} \qquad I = \frac{E}{R} = \frac{P}{E} = \sqrt{\frac{P}{R}}$$

$$R = \frac{E}{I} = \frac{E^2}{P} = \frac{P}{I^2} \qquad P = I^2R = \frac{E^2}{R} = EI$$

2. Resistance in Series
$$R_T = R_1 + R_2 + R_3 + R_4 + ...$$

3. Resistance in Parallel
$$\frac{1}{R_T} = \frac{1}{R_1} + \frac{1}{R_2} + \frac{1}{R_3} + ...$$

$$R_T = \frac{R_1 \times R_2}{R_1 + R_2} \quad (For\ 2\ Resistors\ Only)$$

$$R_T = \frac{R_1}{\#\ of\ Resistors} \quad (For\ Equal\ Resistors)$$

4. Capacitance in Series
Computed like resistance in Parallel.

5. Capacitance in Parallel
Computed like resistance in Series.

6. Inductance in Series
Computed like resistance in Series.

7. Inductance in Parallel
Computed like resistance in Parallel.

8. Capacitive Reactance

$$X_C = \frac{1}{2 \pi f C} \quad (f = Frequency\ in\ Hz)$$

9. Inductive Reactance
$$X_L = 2 \pi f L \quad (f = Frequency\ in\ Hz)$$

10. Noise Index
$$db = 20 \times \log_{10} \frac{Noise\ Voltage\ (over\ a\ 1\ decade\ bandwith)}{DC\ Voltage}$$

11. Parts Per Million (ppm): Conversion of % to ppm

%	ppm	%	ppm
0.0001%	1	0.01%	100
0.0002%	2	0.02%	200
0.0005%	5	0.025%	250
0.001%	10	0.05%	500
0.0025%	25	0.1%	1,000
0.005%	50	1.0%	10,000

Formula is: $\dfrac{0.0001\% \times 10^6}{100} = 1 \text{ ppm}$

12. Frequency (f)

$$f = \frac{1}{2\pi\sqrt{LC}}$$

NOTES:

Index

Notes

Printed in Great Britain
by Amazon

39072731R00076